Ancient Achievements

Student Workbook | Part 1

SpellingYouSee™

Building Confidence

A Demme Learning Publication

Ancient Achievements Student Workbook, Parts 1 and 2

©2014 Spelling You See
©2013 Karen J. Holinga, PhD.
Published and distributed by Demme Learning

www.SpellingYouSee.com

1-888-854-6284 or +1 717-283-1448 | www.demmelearning.com
Lancaster, Pennsylvania USA

ISBN 978-1-60826-621-0 (Ancient Achievements Student Workbook)
ISBN 978-1-60826-622-7 (Part 1)

Printed in the United States of America

1   14   1014

To the Instructor

This innovative program is designed to help your student become a confident and successful speller. The program is not difficult, but it is different. Your *Instructor's Handbook* is essential in order to teach this program effectively.

Before you begin, take time to read **Getting Started** in the *Handbook* and the directions for the first lesson. This level of Spelling You See has a new feature called a Spotlight. The Spotlights are designed to introduce the student to Word Extension, the stage of spelling that follows Skill Development. The *Handbook* provides suggestions for optional activities designed to extend the ideas in the Spotlights. There is an answer key in the back of the *Handbook* that shows exactly how each passage in the student book should be marked.

For a more in-depth understanding of the program, read the sections about the philosophy and the developmental stages of spelling. You may also find the answers to **Frequently Asked Questions** helpful.

1.   Read the passage aloud to your instructor. The word Lascaux is pronounced la-SKO.

2.   Vowel chunks are a combination of vowels that usually make one sound. Find the **vowel chunks** in the passage and mark them using a yellow colored pencil or highlighter. Not all of the vowel chunks on the list will be in the passage.

Vowel Chunks

aa ae ai ao au aw ay	oa oe oi oo ou ow oy
ea ee ei eo eu ew ey eau	ua ue ui uo uu uy
ia ie ii io iu	

The Cave of Lascaux is one of the most famous caves in the world. One day, four French teenagers were exploring. When the boys eased into a hidden cave, they were shocked! It was painted! Bison, deer, horses, cows, and bulls seemed to leap across the cave walls and ceilings. Some pictures showed people hunting animals. Thousands of years before, ancient people had painted these pictures. They had used minerals to make paints. They left behind a visual treasure.

Ancient Achievements

Copy and chunk the passage. Look at the opposite page if you need help.

The Cave of Lascaux is one of the most

The Cave of Lasscaux is one of the most

famous caves in the world. One day,

famous caves in the world. One day,

four French teenagers were exploring.

four french teenagers were exploring.

When the boys eased into a hidden cave,

When the boys eased into a hidden cave,

they were shocked! It was painted!

they were shocked! It was painted!

Bison, deer, horses, cows, and bulls

Bison, deer, horses, cows and bulls

seemed to leap across the cave walls

seemed to leap across the cave walls

and ceilings. Some pictures showed

and ceilings. Some pictures showed

people hunting animals.

people hunting animals.

8-8-16 ✓

1. Read the passage aloud to your instructor.

2. Find the **vowel chunks** in the passage and mark them in yellow.

Vowel Chunks

aa ae ai ao au aw ay	oa oe oi oo ou ow oy
ea ee ei eo eu ew ey eau	ua ue ui uo uu uy
ia ie ii io iu	

The Cave of Lascaux is one of the most famous caves in the world. One day, four French teenagers were exploring. When the boys eased into a hidden cave, they were shocked! It was painted! Bison, deer, horses, cows, and bulls seemed to leap across the cave walls and ceilings. Some pictures showed people hunting animals. Thousands of years before, ancient people had painted these pictures. They had used minerals to make paints. They left behind a visual treasure.

Copy and chunk the passage. Look at the opposite page if you need help.

When the boys eased into a hidden cave,

When the boys eased into a hidden cave,

they were shocked! It was painted!

they were shocked! It was painted!

Bison, deer, horses, cows, and bulls

Bison, deer, horses, cows, and bulls

seemed to leap across the cave walls and

seemed to leap across the cave walls and

ceilings. Some pictures showed people

ceilings. Some pictures showed people

hunting animals. Thousands of years

hunting animals. Thousands of years

before, ancient people had painted these

before, ancient people had painted these

pictures. They had used minerals to make

pictures. They had used minerals to mak

paints. They left behind a visual treasure.

paints. they left behind a visual treshure.

8-90-16

1. Read the passage aloud to your instructor.

2. Find the <u>**vowel chunks**</u> in the passage and mark them in yellow.

3. Read and think about the Spotlight on this page.

Vowel Chunks

aa ae ai ao au aw ay	oa oe oi oo ou ow oy
ea ee ei eo eu ew ey eau	ua ue ui uo uu uy
ia ie ii io iu	

The Cave of Lascaux is one of the most famous caves in the world. One day, four French teenagers were exploring. When the boys eased into a hidden cave, they were shocked! It was painted! Bison, deer, horses, cows, and bulls seemed to leap across the cave walls and ceilings. Some pictures showed people hunting animals. Thousands of years before, ancient people had painted these pictures. They had used minerals to make paints. They left behind a visual treasure.

SPOTLIGHT

Looking for rhyming words with the same letter patterns as the words in the passage can help you become a better speller. For example, the word *faint* has the same vowel chunk and ending consonant as the word *paint* in this passage. Perhaps some people felt *faint* with surprise when they saw the *paint* on the cave walls. Be careful—not all rhyming words have matching letter patterns. That is why it is so important to look at words carefully as you work your way through *Ancient Achievements*.

Copy and chunk the passage. Look at the opposite page if you need help.

The Cave of Lascaux is one of the most

The Cave of Lascaux is one of the most

famous caves in the world. One day,

famous caves in the world. One day,

four French teenagers were exploring.

four french teenagers were exploring.

When the boys eased into a hidden cave,

When the boys eased into a hidden cave,

they were shocked! It was painted!

they were shocked! It was painted!

Bison, deer, horses, cows, and bulls

Bison, deer, horses, cows, and bulls

seemed to leap across the cave walls

Seemed to leap across the cave walls

and ceilings. Some pictures showed

and ceilings. Some pictures showed

people hunting animals.

people hunting animals.

8/10

1. Read the passage aloud to your instructor.

2. Find the **vowel chunks** in the passage and mark them in yellow.

    All of the passages in this workbook are also in the **Resources** section in the *Instructor's Handbook*. For dictation, you may want to cover this page with a piece of paper while your instructor reads the passage from the *Handbook*.

Vowel Chunks

aa ae ai ao au aw ay	oa oe oi oo ou ow oy
ea ee ei eo eu ew ey eau	ua ue ui uo uu uy
ia ie ii io iu	

The Cave of Lascaux is one of the most famous caves in the world. One day, four French teenagers were exploring. When the boys eased into a hidden cave, they were shocked! It was painted! Bison, deer, horses, cows, and bulls seemed to leap across the cave walls and ceilings. Some pictures showed people hunting animals. Thousands of years before, ancient people had painted these pictures. They had used minerals to make paints. They left behind a visual treasure.

Write this week's passage from dictation. Ask for help if you need it.

The cave of Lacaux is one of the moast famous caves in the world. One day four french kids were exploring when the boys wonderd into a cave they were shocked! It was painted! Bison, deer, horses, cows and bulls seemed to leap out from the cave walls and cellings. Some pictures showed people hunting anamils. thousands of years before, a short people had painted these pictures, They had used matriles to make paints. they left behind a visual treshure

8/12

1. Read the passage aloud to your instructor.

2. Find the **vowel chunks** in the passage and mark them in yellow.

Vowel Chunks

aa ae ai ao au aw ay	oa oe oi oo ou ow oy
ea ee ei eo eu ew ey eau	ua ue ui uo uu uy
ia ie ii io iu	

The Cave of Lascaux is one of the most famous caves in the world. One day, four French teenagers were exploring. When the boys eased into a hidden cave, they were shocked! It was painted! Bison, deer, horses, cows, and bulls seemed to leap across the cave walls and ceilings. Some pictures showed people hunting animals. Thousands of years before, ancient people had painted these pictures. They had used minerals to make paints. They left behind a visual treasure.

Section 2: Second Dictation

See if you can write this week's passage from dictation without asking for help.

the cave of lacaux is one of the most famous caves in the world one day four french boys were exploring when the boys wonderd into a cave they were shocked on the walls was painted byson, deer, horses, cows and bulls seemed to leap across the walls and celling some pictures showed people hunting thousands of years before achent people had painted these they used minnards to make paint they had left behind visual treshure

8/15

1. Read the passage aloud to your instructor.

2. Find the **vowel chunks** in the passage and mark them in yellow.

Vowel Chunks

aa ae ai ao au aw ay	oa oe oi oo ou ow oy
ea ee ei eo eu ew ey eau	ua ue ui uo uu uy
ia ie ii io iu	

An airplane was flying over the German countryside near Goseck. The pilot saw a large circle in the wheat fields below. People had noticed similar circles before. Their purpose was a mystery. A group of young archeologists studied the Goseck Circle. They found four circles inside each other. One was a mound, and one was a ditch. Two of them were once marked with wooden fences. The gates in the fences lined up with the sun on certain days of the year. The circles may have helped people keep track of the seasons.

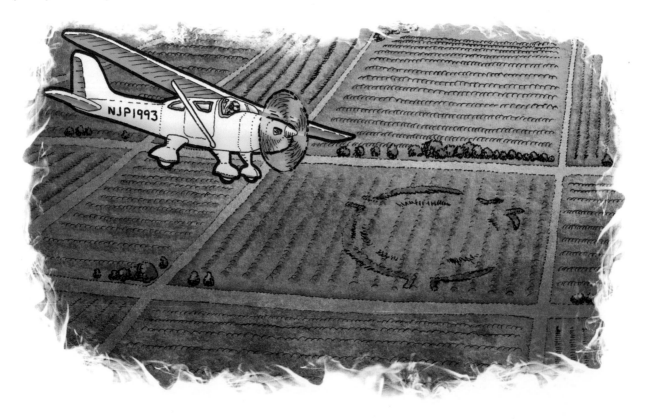

Copy and chunk the passage. Look at the opposite page if you need help.

An airplane was flying over the German

An airplane was flying over the German

countryside near Goseck. The pilot saw

countryside near Gooseck. The pilot saw

a large circle in the wheat fields below.

a large circle in the wheat fields below,

People had noticed similar circles before.

people had noticed similar circles before.

Their purpose was a mystery. A group

Their purpouse was a mystery. A group

# of young archeologists studied the

of young archeologists studied the

Goseck Circle. They found four circles

Goseck circles. They found four circles

inside each other. One was a mound,

inside each other One was a mound,

and one was a ditch.

and one was a ditch.

8/16

1.   Read the passage aloud to your instructor.

2.   Find the **vowel chunks** in the passage and mark them in yellow.

Vowel Chunks

aa ae ai ao au aw ay	oa oe oi oo ou ow oy
ea ee ei eo eu ew ey eau	ua ue ui uo uu uy
ia ie ii io iu	

An airplane was flying over the German countryside near Goseck. The pilot saw a large circle in the wheat fields below. People had noticed similar circles before. Their purpose was a mystery. A group of young archeologists studied the Goseck Circle. They found four circles inside each other. One was a mound, and one was a ditch. Two of them were once marked with wooden fences. The gates in the fences lined up with the sun on certain days of the year. The circles may have helped people keep track of the seasons.

Copy and chunk the passage. Look at the opposite page if you need help.

A group of young archeologists studied

A group of young archeologists studied

the Goseck Circle. They found four

the Goseck Circle. They found four

circles inside each other. One was a

circles inside each other. One was a

mound, and one was a ditch. Two of them

mound, and one was a ditch. Two of them

were once marked with wooden

were once marked with wooden

fences. The gates in the fences lined up

fences. The gates in the fences lined up

with the sun on certain days of the year.

with the sun on certain days of the year.

The circles may have helped people keep

The circles many have helped people keep

track of the seasons.

track of the seasons.

8/17

1. Read the passage aloud to your instructor.

2. Find the **vowel chunks** in the passage and mark them in yellow.

3. Read the Spotlight. The *Instructor's Handbook* has more information about the topics in the Spotlights.

Vowel Chunks

aa ae ai ao au aw ay	oa oe oi oo ou ow oy
ea ee ei eo eu ew ey eau	ua ue ui uo uu uy
ia ie ii io iu	

An airplane was flying over the German countryside near Goseck. The pilot saw a large circle in the wheat fields below. People had noticed similar circles before. Their purpose was a mystery. A group of young archeologists studied the Goseck Circle. They found four circles inside each other. One was a mound, and one was a ditch. Two of them were once marked with wooden fences. The gates in the fences lined up with the sun on certain days of the year. The circles may have helped people keep track of the seasons.

SPOTLIGHT

Many English words have roots that come from other languages. The word *archeology* comes from Greek words that mean "the study of ancient things." An *archeologist* studies ancient people by looking at old buildings, tools, and other items they have left behind. Watch for the *-ology* pattern in other words. For example, *biology* means "the study of life", and *geology* means "the study of the earth."

Copy and chunk the passage. Look at the opposite page if you need help.

An airplane was flying over the German

An airplane was flying over the German

countryside near Goseck. The pilot saw

countryside near Goseck. The pilot saw

a large circle in the wheat fields below.

a large circle in the wheat fields below.

People had noticed similar circles before.

people had noticed similar circles before.

Their purpose was a mystery. A group

Their purpoose was a mystrey. A group

# of young archeologists studied the

of young archeologists studied the

Goseck Circle. They found four circles

boseck circle. They found four circles

inside each other. One was a mound,

inside each other. One was a mound,

and one was a ditch.

and one was a ditch.

8/18

1. Read the passage aloud to your instructor.

2. Find the **vowel chunks** in the passage and mark them in yellow.

Vowel Chunks

aa ae ai ao au aw ay	oa oe oi oo ou ow oy
ea ee ei eo eu ew ey eau	ua ue ui uo uu uy
ia ie ii io iu	

An airplane was flying over the German countryside near Goseck. The pilot saw a large circle in the wheat fields below. People had noticed similar circles before. Their purpose was a mystery. A group of young archeologists studied the Goseck Circle. They found four circles inside each other. One was a mound, and one was a ditch. Two of them were once marked with wooden fences. The gates in the fences lined up with the sun on certain days of the year. The circles may have helped people keep track of the seasons.

Write this week's passage from dictation. Ask for help if you need it.

An airplane was flying over germney outside of Goosheck the pilot swa a large circle in the crops below a group of young archoligests studied the circles they found circles inside of circles with woden fences the fences lined up with the sun on certen days the circles may have healped peeple ceep track of seasons

8/22

1. Read the passage aloud to your instructor.

2. Find the **vowel chunks** in the passage and mark them in yellow.

Vowel Chunks

aa ae ai ao au aw ay	oa oe oi oo ou ow oy
ea ee ei eo eu ew ey eau	ua ue ui uo uu uy
ia ie ii io iu	

An airplane was flying over the German countryside near Goseck. The pilot saw a large circle in the wheat fields below. People had noticed similar circles before. Their purpose was a mystery. A group of young archeologists studied the Goseck Circle. They found four circles inside each other. One was a mound, and one was a ditch. Two of them were once marked with wooden fences. The gates in the fences lined up with the sun on certain days of the year. The circles may have helped people keep track of the seasons.

See if you can write this week's passage from dictation without asking for help.

An airplane was flying over the german country side the pilot saw large circles in the fields below people noticed simmlar circles before. there poprous was unknown a group of young archoligsts studied studies them and figurer out they were for navagation

8/26

1. Read the passage aloud to your instructor.

2. Find the <u>**consonant chunks**</u> in the passage and mark them in blue. Notice that a consonant chunk may have a different sound than the individual letters do.

Consonant Chunks

ch gh sh ph th wh wr gn kn dg qu ck tch bb cc dd ff	
gg hh kk ll mm nn pp rr ss tt ww vv zz	

Thousands of years ago, the Sumerians created a system of writing. It is called cuneiform. That's an odd name, but it actually makes sense. The name comes from the Latin word *cuneus*. It means *wedge*. The Sumerians used a wedge-shaped writing tool. They pressed this tool into damp clay tablets. Then the tablets were baked in the scorching sun. Writing was not the quick and easy process it is today. Some tablets lasted a long time. As a result, we know more about how people lived long ago.

Copy and chunk the passage. Look at the opposite page if you need help.

Thousands of years ago, the Sumerians

Thousands of years ago, the Sumerians

created a system of writing. It is called

created a system of wrighting. I tis called

cuneiform. That's an odd name, but it

cuneiform. thats an odd name, but it

actually makes sense. The name comes

actually makes sense. The mame comes

from the Latin word <u>cuneus</u>. It means

from the latin word cuneus It means

<u>wedge</u>. The Sumerians used a wedge-

wedge. The Sumerians used a wedge-

shaped writing tool. They pressed this

shaped writing tool. they pressed this

tool into damp clay tablets. Then the

tool into damp clay tablets. then the

tablets were baked in the scorching sun.

tablets were baked in the scorching sun.

8/29

3B

Section 1: Consonant Chunks

1. Read the passage aloud to your instructor.

2. Find the **consonant chunks** in the passage and mark them in blue.

Consonant Chunks

ch gh sh ph th wh wr gn kn dg qu ck tch bb cc dd ff
gg hh kk ll mm nn pp rr ss tt ww vv zz

Thousands of years ago, the Sumerians created a system of writing. It is called cuneiform. That's an odd name, but it actually makes sense. The name comes from the Latin word *cuneus*. It means *wedge*. The Sumerians used a wedge-shaped writing tool. They pressed this tool into damp clay tablets. Then the tablets were baked in the scorching sun. Writing was not the quick and easy process it is today. Some tablets lasted a long time. As a result, we know more about how people lived long ago.

Copy and chunk the passage. Look at the opposite page if you need help.

It means <u>wedge</u>. The Sumerians used a

It means wedge. The Sumerians used a

wedge-shaped writing tool. They pressed

wedge shaped writing tool. They pressed

this tool into damp clay tablets. Then the

this tool into damp clay tablets Then the

tablets were baked in the scorching sun.

tablets were banked in the scorching sun

Writing was not the quick and easy

writing was not the quick and easy

process it is today. Some tablets lasted a

prosess it is today. Some tablets lasted a

long time. As a result, we know more

long time. As a result we know more

about how people lived long ago.

about how people lived long ago.

8/30

1. Read the passage aloud to your instructor.

2. Find the **consonant chunks** in the passage and mark them in blue.

3. Read the Spotlight.

Consonant Chunks

| ch gh sh ph th wh wr gn kn dg qu ck tch bb cc dd ff |
| gg hh kk ll mm nn pp rr ss tt ww vv zz |

Thousands of years ago, the Sumerians created a system of writing. It is called cuneiform. That's an odd name, but it actually makes sense. The name comes from the Latin word *cuneus*. It means *wedge*. The Sumerians used a wedge-shaped writing tool. They pressed this tool into damp clay tablets. Then the tablets were baked in the scorching sun. Writing was not the quick and easy process it is today. Some tablets lasted a long time. As a result, we know more about how people lived long ago.

SPOTLIGHT

Some English words have roots that come from Latin words. Often words that come from Latin or Greek are used when talking about science, medicine, and other technical subjects. *Cuneiform* writing is wedge-shaped writing. There are three bones in the human foot called *cuneiform* bones. How do you think they are shaped?

Copy and chunk the passage. Look at the opposite page if you need help.

Thousands of years ago, the Sumerians

Thousands of years ago, the Sumerians

created a system of writing. It is called

created a system of wrichting. It is called

cuneiform. That's an odd name, but it

cuneiform. That's an odd name, but it

actually makes sense. The name comes

actually makes sense. The name comes

from the Latin word <u>cuneus</u>. It means

from the latin word <u>cuneus</u> It means

<u>wedge</u>. The Sumerians used a wedge-

<u>wedge</u> The sumerians used a wedge-

shaped writing tool. They pressed this

shaped writing tool. They pressed this

tool into damp clay tablets. Then the

tool into damp lday tablets. Then the

tablets were baked in the scorching sun.

tablets were baked in the scorching sun.

9/31

1. Read the passage aloud to your instructor.

2. Find the **<u>consonant chunks</u>** in the passage and mark them in blue.

Consonant Chunks

ch	gh	sh	ph	th	wh	wr	gn	kn	dg	qu	ck	tch	bb	cc	dd	ff
gg	hh	kk	ll	mm	nn	pp	rr	ss	tt	ww	vv	zz				

Thousands of years ago, the Sumerians created a system of writing. It is called cuneiform. That's an odd name, but it actually makes sense. The name comes from the Latin word *cuneus*. It means *wedge*. The Sumerians used a wedge-shaped writing tool. They pressed this tool into damp clay tablets. Then the tablets were baked in the scorching sun. Writing was not the quick and easy process it is today. Some tablets lasted a long time. As a result, we know more about how people lived long ago.

Write this week's passage from dictation. Ask for help if you need it.

Thousands of years ago the Sumarians created a system of wrighting it is called cuneiform. Thats an odd name but it actuly makes sence the name comes from a latan word for wedge the sumarians used a wedge shaped tool to press figurs in to wet clay tablets then fired to harden them

9/2

1. Read the passage aloud to your instructor.

2. Find the **<u>consonant chunks</u>** in the passage and mark them in blue.

Consonant Chunks

ch	gh	sh	ph	th	wh	wr	gn	kn	dg	qu	ck	tch	bb	cc	dd	ff
gg	hh	kk	ll	mm	nn	pp	rr	ss	tt	ww	vv	zz				

Thousands of years ago, the Sumerians created a system of writing. It is called cuneiform. That's an odd name, but it actually makes sense. The name comes from the Latin word *cuneus*. It means *wedge*. The Sumerians used a wedge-shaped writing tool. They pressed this tool into damp clay tablets. Then the tablets were baked in the scorching sun. Writing was not the quick and easy process it is today. Some tablets lasted a long time. As a result, we know more about how people lived long ago.

Section 2: Second Dictation

See if you can write this week's passage from dictation without asking for help.

1. Read the passage aloud to your instructor.

2. Find the **consonant chunks** in the passage and mark them in blue.

Consonant Chunks

ch	gh	sh	ph	th	wh	wr	gn	kn	dg	qu	ck	tch	bb	cc	dd	ff
gg	hh	kk	ll	mm	nn	pp	rr	ss	tt	ww	vv	zz				

The ancient Chinese had a secret. A person who shared the secret with others might be killed. This hidden knowledge started with a moth and a tree. Each moth laid eggs that produced silkworms. Each silkworm ate mulberry leaves. The worm produced a long, thin thread. The thread formed a cocoon. Women learned to harvest the cocoons at just the right time. They wove the threads into fine silk. For centuries, the Chinese guarded this secret. They traded their precious silk for other valuable products.

Copy and chunk the passage. Look at the opposite page if you need help.

The ancient Chinese had a secret. A

The

person who shared the secret with

others might be killed. This hidden

knowledge started with a moth and a

tree. Each moth laid eggs that produced

silkworms. Each silkworm ate mulberry

leaves. The worm produced a long, thin

thread. The thread formed a cocoon.

Women learned to harvest the cocoons.

1. Read the passage aloud to your instructor.

2. Find the **consonant chunks** in the passage and mark them in blue.

Consonant Chunks

ch	gh	sh	ph	th	wh	wr	gn	kn	dg	qu	ck	tch	bb	cc	dd	ff
gg	hh	kk	ll	mm	nn	pp	rr	ss	tt	ww	vv	zz				

The ancient Chinese had a secret. A person who shared the secret with others might be killed. This hidden knowledge started with a moth and a tree. Each moth laid eggs that produced silkworms. Each silkworm ate mulberry leaves. The worm produced a long, thin thread. The thread formed a cocoon. Women learned to harvest the cocoons at just the right time. They wove the threads into fine silk. For centuries, the Chinese guarded this secret. They traded their precious silk for other valuable products.

Copy and chunk the passage. Look at the opposite page if you need help.

Each silkworm ate mulberry leaves.

Each

The worm produced a long, thin

thread. The thread formed a cocoon.

Women learned to harvest the cocoons

at just the right time. They wove the

threads into fine silk. For centuries, the

Chinese guarded this secret. They

traded their precious silk for other

valuable products.

1.   Read the passage aloud to your instructor.

2.   Find the **consonant chunks** in the passage and mark them in blue.

3.   Read the Spotlight.

Consonant Chunks

| ch gh sh ph th wh wr gn kn dg qu ck tch bb cc dd ff |
| gg hh kk ll mm nn pp rr ss tt ww vv zz |

The ancient Chinese had a secret. A person who shared the secret with others might be killed. This hidden knowledge started with a moth and a tree. Each moth laid eggs that produced silkworms. Each silkworm ate mulberry leaves. The worm produced a long, thin thread. The thread formed a cocoon. Women learned to harvest the cocoons at just the right time. They wove the threads into fine silk. For centuries, the Chinese guarded this secret. They traded their precious silk for other valuable products.

SPOTLIGHT

Do you see the word *cent* in *centuries*? Both words come from the Latin word for one hundred. A *century* is one hundred years, a *centennial* is a hundredth anniversary, and a *centipede* seems like it must have one hundred legs when it scurries across the floor. Of course, it takes one hundred *cents* to make one dollar and one hundred *centimeters* to make a meter.

Copy and chunk the passage. Look at the opposite page if you need help.

The ancient Chinese had a secret. A

The

person who shared the secret with

others might be killed. This hidden

knowledge started with a moth and a

tree. Each moth laid eggs that produced

silkworms. Each silkworm ate mulberry

leaves. The worm produced a long, thin

thread. The thread formed a cocoon.

Women learned to harvest the cocoons.

1. Read the passage aloud to your instructor.

2. Find the **consonant chunks** in the passage and mark them in blue.

Consonant Chunks

ch	gh	sh	ph	th	wh	wr	gn	kn	dg	qu	ck	tch	bb	cc	dd ff
gg	hh	kk	ll	mm	nn	pp	rr	ss	tt	ww	vv	zz			

The ancient Chinese had a secret. A person who shared the secret with others might be killed. This hidden knowledge started with a moth and a tree. Each moth laid eggs that produced silkworms. Each silkworm ate mulberry leaves. The worm produced a long, thin thread. The thread formed a cocoon. Women learned to harvest the cocoons at just the right time. They wove the threads into fine silk. For centuries, the Chinese guarded this secret. They traded their precious silk for other valuable products.

Ancient Achievements

Write this week's passage from dictation. Ask for help if you need it.

The

1. Read the passage aloud to your instructor.

2. Find the <u>**consonant chunks**</u> in the passage and mark them in blue.

Consonant Chunks

ch	gh	sh	ph	th	wh	wr	gn	kn	dg	qu	ck	tch	bb	cc	dd	ff

gg	hh	kk	ll	mm	nn	pp	rr	ss	tt	ww	vv	zz

The ancient Chinese had a secret. A person who shared the secret with others might be killed. This hidden knowledge started with a moth and a tree. Each moth laid eggs that produced silkworms. Each silkworm ate mulberry leaves. The worm produced a long, thin thread. The thread formed a cocoon. Women learned to harvest the cocoons at just the right time. They wove the threads into fine silk. For centuries, the Chinese guarded this secret. They traded their precious silk for other valuable products.

Section 2: Second Dictation

See if you can write this week's passage from dictation without asking for help.

1. Read the passage aloud to your instructor.

2. Mark the **vowel chunks** in yellow and the **consonant chunks** in blue.

Vowel Chunks
aa ae ai ao au aw ay
ea ee ei eo eu ew ey eau
ia ie ii io iu
oa oe oi oo ou ow oy
ua ue ui uo uu uy

Consonant Chunks
ch gh sh ph th wh
wr gn kn dg qu ck
tch bb cc dd ff gg
hh kk ll mm nn pp
rr ss tt ww vv zz

Ancient Egyptians believed it was important not to let a body decay after death. Rich people preserved bodies with great care. First, the brain was removed and discarded as worthless. Some organs were saved in jars. The heart was left in the body. To Egyptians, the heart was the center of reason. They washed the body and packed it in salts to dry. Weeks later, they wrapped it in cloth. Finally, they placed this mummy in a special coffin. The coffin was placed inside one or more larger coffins.

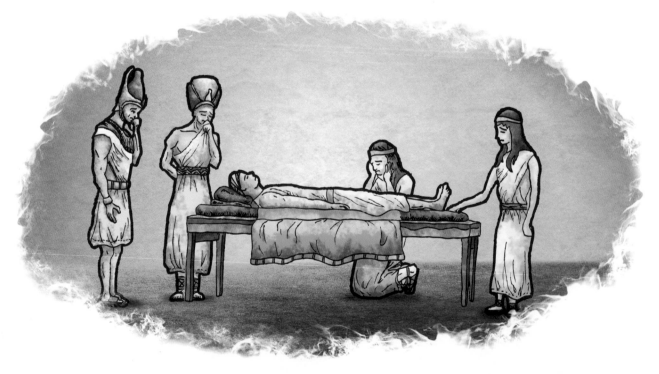

Copy and chunk the passage. Look at the opposite page if you need help.

Ancient Egyptians believed it was

Ancient

important not to let a body decay after

death. Rich people preserved bodies with

great care. First, the brain was removed

and discarded as worthless. Some organs

were saved in jars. The heart was left in

the body. To Egyptians, the heart was the

center of reason. They washed the body

and packed it in salts to dry.

1. Read the passage aloud to your instructor.

2. Mark the **vowel chunks** in yellow and the **consonant chunks** in blue.

Vowel Chunks
aa ae ai ao au aw ay
ea ee ei eo eu ew ey eau
ia ie ii io iu
oa oe oi oo ou ow oy
ua ue ui uo uu uy

Consonant Chunks
ch gh sh ph th wh
wr gn kn dg qu ck
tch bb cc dd ff gg
hh kk ll mm nn pp
rr ss tt ww vv zz

Ancient Egyptians believed it was important not to let a body decay after death. Rich people preserved bodies with great care. First, the brain was removed and discarded as worthless. Some organs were saved in jars. The heart was left in the body. To Egyptians, the heart was the center of reason. They washed the body and packed it in salts to dry. Weeks later, they wrapped it in cloth. Finally, they placed this mummy in a special coffin. The coffin was placed inside one or more larger coffins.

Copy and chunk the passage. Look at the opposite page if you need help.

Some organs were saved in jars. The

Some

heart was left in the body. To Egyptians,

the heart was the center of reason.

They washed the body and packed it in

salts to dry. Weeks later, they wrapped

it in cloth. Finally, they placed this

mummy in a special coffin. The coffin

was placed inside one or more larger

coffins.

1. Read the passage aloud to your instructor.

2. Mark the <u>vowel chunks</u> in yellow and the <u>consonant chunks</u> in blue.

3. Read the Spotlight.

Vowel Chunks
aa ae ai ao au aw ay
ea ee ei eo eu ew ey eau
ia ie ii io iu
oa oe oi oo ou ow oy
ua ue ui uo uu uy

Consonant Chunks
ch gh sh ph th wh
wr gn kn dg qu ck
tch bb cc dd ff gg
hh kk ll mm nn pp
rr ss tt ww vv zz

Ancient Egyptians believed it was important not to let a body decay after death. Rich people preserved bodies with great care. First, the brain was removed and discarded as worthless. Some organs were saved in jars. The heart was left in the body. To Egyptians, the heart was the center of reason. They washed the body and packed it in salts to dry. Weeks later, they wrapped it in cloth. Finally, they placed this mummy in a special coffin. The coffin was placed inside one or more larger coffins.

SPOTLIGHT

The combination *th* is a very common consonant chunk. In Old English, two separate symbols were used for sounds similar to our *th*. The first books to be printed with moveable type were not in English. When books began to be printed in English, the letters *th* were substituted for the English þ and ð symbols.

Copy and chunk the passage. Look at the opposite page if you need help.

Ancient Egyptians believed it was

Ancient

important not to let a body decay after

death. Rich people preserved bodies with

great care. First, the brain was removed

and discarded as worthless. Some organs

were saved in jars. The heart was left in

the body. To Egyptians, the heart was the

center of reason. They washed the body

and packed it in salts to dry.

1. Read the passage aloud to your instructor.

2. Mark the **vowel chunks** in yellow and the **consonant chunks** in blue.

Vowel Chunks	Consonant Chunks
aa ae ai ao au aw ay	ch gh sh ph th wh
ea ee ei eo eu ew ey eau	wr gn kn dg qu ck
ia ie ii io iu	tch bb cc dd ff gg
oa oe oi oo ou ow oy	hh kk ll mm nn pp
ua ue ui uo uu uy	rr ss tt ww vv zz

Ancient Egyptians believed it was important not to let a body decay after death. Rich people preserved bodies with great care. First, the brain was removed and discarded as worthless. Some organs were saved in jars. The heart was left in the body. To Egyptians, the heart was the center of reason. They washed the body and packed it in salts to dry. Weeks later, they wrapped it in cloth. Finally, they placed this mummy in a special coffin. The coffin was placed inside one or more larger coffins.

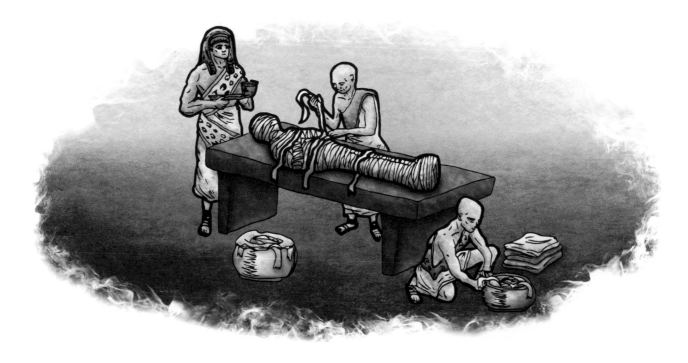

Write this week's passage from dictation. Ask for help if you need it.

Ancient

1. Read the passage aloud to your instructor.

2. Mark the **vowel chunks** in yellow and the **consonant chunks** in blue.

Vowel Chunks	Consonant Chunks
aa ae ai ao au aw ay	ch gh sh ph th wh
ea ee ei eo eu ew ey eau	wr gn kn dg qu ck
ia ie ii io iu	tch bb cc dd ff gg
oa oe oi oo ou ow oy	hh kk ll mm nn pp
ua ue ui uo uu uy	rr ss tt ww vv zz

Ancient Egyptians believed it was important not to let a body decay after death. Rich people preserved bodies with great care. First, the brain was removed and discarded as worthless. Some organs were saved in jars. The heart was left in the body. To Egyptians, the heart was the center of reason. They washed the body and packed it in salts to dry. Weeks later, they wrapped it in cloth. Finally, they placed this mummy in a special coffin. The coffin was placed inside one or more larger coffins.

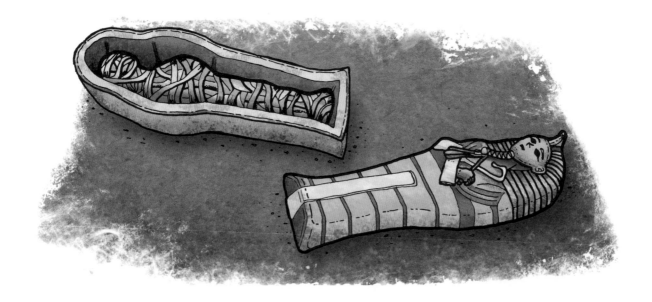

Section 2: Second Dictation

See if you can write this week's passage from dictation without asking for help.

1. Read the passage aloud to your instructor.

2. Mark the **vowel chunks** in yellow and the **consonant chunks** in blue.

Vowel Chunks	Consonant Chunks
aa ae ai ao au aw ay	ch gh sh ph th wh
ea ee ei eo eu ew ey eau	wr gn kn dg qu ck
ia ie ii io iu	tch bb cc dd ff gg
oa oe oi oo ou ow oy	hh kk ll mm nn pp
ua ue ui uo uu uy	rr ss tt ww vv zz

"Time laughs at all things, but the pyramids laugh at time." That old saying seems true. Some pyramids have lasted so long they must be laughing! The Great Pyramid in Egypt was built thousands of years ago. Many other famous buildings are gone, but the Great Pyramid remains. It is massive. Its base covers 13 acres. It contains more than two million limestone and granite blocks. Some of the blocks weigh over two tons. It was built to house the pharaoh's body forever.

Copy and chunk the passage. Look at the opposite page if you need help.

"Time laughs at all things, but the

"Time

pyramids laugh at time." That old saying

seems true. Some pyramids have lasted

so long they must be laughing! The

Great Pyramid in Egypt was built

thousands of years ago. Many other

famous buildings are gone, but the

Great Pyramid remains. It is massive.

Its base covers 13 acres.

1.   Read the passage aloud to your instructor.

2.   Mark the **vowel chunks** in yellow and the **consonant chunks** in blue.

Vowel Chunks
aa ae ai ao au aw ay
ea ee ei eo eu ew ey eau
ia ie ii io iu
oa oe oi oo ou ow oy
ua ue ui uo uu uy

Consonant Chunks
ch gh sh ph th wh
wr gn kn dg qu ck
tch bb cc dd ff gg
hh kk ll mm nn pp
rr ss tt ww vv zz

"Time laughs at all things, but the pyramids laugh at time." That old saying seems true. Some pyramids have lasted so long they must be laughing! The Great Pyramid in Egypt was built thousands of years ago. Many other famous buildings are gone, but the Great Pyramid remains. It is massive. Its base covers 13 acres. It contains more than two million limestone and granite blocks. Some of the blocks weigh over two tons. It was built to house the pharaoh's body forever.

Copy and chunk the passage. Look at the opposite page if you need help.

The Great Pyramid in Egypt was built

The

thousands of years ago. Many other

famous buildings are gone, but the

Great Pyramid remains. It is massive.

Its base covers 13 acres. It contains

more than two million limestone and

granite blocks. Some of the blocks weigh

over two tons. It was built to house the

pharaoh's body forever.

1. Read the passage aloud to your instructor.

2. Mark the **vowel chunks** in yellow and the **consonant chunks** in blue.

3. Read the Spotlight. The *Instructor's Handbook* has more information about the size of the Great Pyramid.

Vowel Chunks	Consonant Chunks
aa ae ai ao au aw ay	ch gh sh ph th wh
ea ee ei eo eu ew ey eau	wr gn kn dg qu ck
ia ie ii io iu	tch bb cc dd ff gg
oa oe oi oo ou ow oy	hh kk ll mm nn pp
ua ue ui uo uu uy	rr ss tt ww vv zz

"Time laughs at all things, but the pyramids laugh at time." That old saying seems true. Some pyramids have lasted so long they must be laughing! The Great Pyramid in Egypt was built thousands of years ago. Many other famous buildings are gone, but the Great Pyramid remains. It is massive. Its base covers 13 acres. It contains more than two million limestone and granite blocks. Some of the blocks weigh over two tons. It was built to house the pharaoh's body forever.

SPOTLIGHT

A compound word is two words combined to make one word. In this lesson, adding *lime* to *stone* makes *limestone*. Limestone is a whitish sedimentary rock. Most limestone is made from shells, corals, and other small sea creatures. It is still used as a building material.

Copy and chunk the passage. Look at the opposite page if you need help.

"Time laughs at all things, but the

"Time

pyramids laugh at time." That old saying

seems true. Some pyramids have lasted

so long they must be laughing! The

Great Pyramid in Egypt was built

thousands of years ago. Many other

famous buildings are gone, but the

Great Pyramid remains. It is massive.

Its base covers 13 acres.

1. Read the passage aloud to your instructor.

2. Mark the <u>**vowel chunks**</u> in yellow and the <u>**consonant chunks**</u> in blue.

Vowel Chunks
aa ae ai ao au aw ay
ea ee ei eo eu ew ey eau
ia ie ii io iu
oa oe oi oo ou ow oy
ua ue ui uo uu uy

Consonant Chunks
ch gh sh ph th wh
wr gn kn dg qu ck
tch bb cc dd ff gg
hh kk ll mm nn pp
rr ss tt ww vv zz

"Time laughs at all things, but the pyramids laugh at time." That old saying seems true. Some pyramids have lasted so long they must be laughing! The Great Pyramid in Egypt was built thousands of years ago. Many other famous buildings are gone, but the Great Pyramid remains. It is massive. Its base covers 13 acres. It contains more than two million limestone and granite blocks. Some of the blocks weigh over two tons. It was built to house the pharaoh's body forever.

Write this week's passage from dictation. Ask for help if you need it.

"Time

1. Read the passage aloud to your instructor.

2. Mark the **vowel chunks** in yellow and the **consonant chunks** in blue.

Vowel Chunks	Consonant Chunks
aa ae ai ao au aw ay	ch gh sh ph th wh
ea ee ei eo eu ew ey eau	wr gn kn dg qu ck
ia ie ii io iu	tch bb cc dd ff gg
oa oe oi oo ou ow oy	hh kk ll mm nn pp
ua ue ui uo uu uy	rr ss tt ww vv zz

"Time laughs at all things, but the pyramids laugh at time." That old saying seems true. Some pyramids have lasted so long they must be laughing! The Great Pyramid in Egypt was built thousands of years ago. Many other famous buildings are gone, but the Great Pyramid remains. It is massive. Its base covers 13 acres. It contains more than two million limestone and granite blocks. Some of the blocks weigh over two tons. It was built to house the pharaoh's body forever.

Section 2: Second Dictation

See if you can write this week's passage from dictation without asking for help.

1. Read the passage aloud to your instructor.

2. Lesson 7 in the *Handbook* explains how Bossy *r* changes the sound of a vowel. Find all the <u>**Bossy *r* chunks**</u> in the passage and mark them in purple.

Bossy *r* Chunks

ar er ir or ur

The first rubber balls were made in Central America. People learned how to gather the sap of the rubber tree. They mixed the sap with the juice of the morning glory vine. When the rubber hardened, it could be used to make many things. Rubber balls were used for games. Many years later, explorers found some of these balls. However, the exact rules of the games are still a mystery.

Copy and chunk the passage. Look at the opposite page if you need help.

The first rubber balls were made in

The

Central America. People learned how to

gather the sap of the rubber tree. They

mixed the sap with the juice of the

morning glory vine. When the rubber

hardened, it could be used to make

many things. Rubber balls were used

for games. Many years later, explorers

found some of these balls.

1. Read the passage aloud to your instructor.

2. Mark the <u>**Bossy *r* chunks**</u> in purple.

Bossy *r* Chunks

ar er ir or ur

The first rubber balls were made in Central America. People learned how to gather the sap of the rubber tree. They mixed the sap with the juice of the morning glory vine. When the rubber hardened, it could be used to make many things. Rubber balls were used for games. Many years later, explorers found some of these balls. However, the exact rules of the games are still a mystery.

Copy and chunk the passage. Look at the opposite page if you need help.

People learned how to gather the sap of

People

the rubber tree. They mixed the sap with

the juice of the morning glory vine.

When the rubber hardened, it could be

used to make many things. Rubber balls

were used for games. Many years later,

explorers found some of these balls.

However, the exact rules of the games

are still a mystery.

1. Read the passage aloud to your instructor.

2. Mark the **Bossy *r* chunks** in purple.

3. Read the Spotlight. Do the activity in the *Handbook* if you wish.

Bossy *r* Chunks

ar er ir or ur

The first rubber balls were made in Central America. People learned how to gather the sap of the rubber tree. They mixed the sap with the juice of the morning glory vine. When the rubber hardened, it could be used to make many things. Rubber balls were used for games. Many years later, explorers found some of these balls. However, the exact rules of the games are still a mystery.

SPOTLIGHT

Have you ever wondered why there are different Bossy *r* chunks? This may seem like a bigger mystery than any story from ancient history. Try reading this sentence aloud and then mark all the Bossy *r* chunks:

"Tom earned a salary teaching the history of pottery in this century."

The *Instructor's Handbook* has directions for a word sorting activity that may help you remember how to spell words that end with a Bossy *r* chunk followed by a *y*.

Copy and chunk the passage. Look at the opposite page if you need help.

The first rubber balls were made in

The

Central America. People learned how to

gather the sap of the rubber tree. They

mixed the sap with the juice of the

morning glory vine. When the rubber

hardened, it could be used to make

many things. Rubber balls were used

for games. Many years later, explorers

found some of these balls.

1. Read the passage aloud to your instructor.

2. Mark the **Bossy *r* chunks** in purple.

Bossy *r* Chunks

ar er ir or ur

The first rubber balls were made in Central America. People learned how to gather the sap of the rubber tree. They mixed the sap with the juice of the morning glory vine. When the rubber hardened, it could be used to make many things. Rubber balls were used for games. Many years later, explorers found some of these balls. However, the exact rules of the games are still a mystery.

Write this week's passage from dictation. Ask for help if you need it.

The

1. Read the passage aloud to your instructor.

2. Mark the **Bossy *r* chunks** in purple.

Bossy *r* Chunks

ar er ir or ur

The first rubber balls were made in Central America. People learned how to gather the sap of the rubber tree. They mixed the sap with the juice of the morning glory vine. When the rubber hardened, it could be used to make many things. Rubber balls were used for games. Many years later, explorers found some of these balls. However, the exact rules of the games are still a mystery.

Section 2: Second Dictation

See if you can write this week's passage from dictation without asking for help.

1. Read the passage aloud to your instructor.

2. Mark the **Bossy _r_ chunks** in purple.

Bossy _r_ Chunks

ar er ir or ur

The Greeks told stories about a war with Troy. After fighting for ten years, both sides were tired of the war. The Greeks made a clever plan. They built an enormous wooden horse. Their best warriors hid inside. The Greeks wheeled the horse to the gates of Troy and pretended to sail away. The people of Troy thought it was a gift. They wheeled the Trojan horse into their city. That was a major blunder! During the night, the Greek warriors slipped out of the Trojan horse and conquered Troy. The story of the Trojan War is still told today.

Copy and chunk the passage. Look at the opposite page if you need help.

The Greeks told stories about a war

The

with Troy. After fighting for ten years,

both sides were tired of the war. The

Greeks made a clever plan. They built an

enormous wooden horse. Their best

warriors hid inside. The Greeks wheeled

the horse to the gates of Troy and

pretended to sail away. The people of

Troy thought it was a gift.

1. Read the passage aloud to your instructor.

2. Mark the <u>**Bossy *r* chunks**</u> in purple.

Bossy *r* Chunks

ar er ir or ur

The Greeks told stories about a war with Troy. After fighting for ten years, both sides were tired of the war. The Greeks made a clever plan. They built an enormous wooden horse. Their best warriors hid inside. The Greeks wheeled the horse to the gates of Troy and pretended to sail away. The people of Troy thought it was a gift. They wheeled the Trojan horse into their city. That was a major blunder! During the night, the Greek warriors slipped out of the Trojan horse and conquered Troy. The story of the Trojan War is still told today.

Copy and chunk the passage. Look at the opposite page if you need help.

The Greeks wheeled the horse to the

The

gates of Troy and pretended to sail

away. The people of Troy thought it was

a gift. They wheeled the Trojan horse

into their city. That was a major blunder!

During the night, the Greek warriors

slipped out of the Trojan horse and

conquered Troy. The story of the Trojan

War is still told today.

1. Read the passage aloud to your instructor.

2. Mark the **Bossy *r* chunks** in purple.

3. Read the Spotlight.

Bossy *r* Chunks

ar er ir or ur

The Greeks told stories about a war with Troy. After fighting for ten years, both sides were tired of the war. The Greeks made a clever plan. They built an enormous wooden horse. Their best warriors hid inside. The Greeks wheeled the horse to the gates of Troy and pretended to sail away. The people of Troy thought it was a gift. They wheeled the Trojan horse into their city. That was a major blunder! During the night, the Greek warriors slipped out of the Trojan horse and conquered Troy. The story of the Trojan War is still told today.

SPOTLIGHT

Words that have *quer* sounded as a single syllable are unusual in American English. The most common ones are *conquer* and its relatives: *conquers, conquered, unconquered, conquering,* and *conqueror.* When you notice an unusual spelling pattern, it is often helpful to think of other words with the same pattern.

Copy and chunk the passage. Look at the opposite page if you need help.

The Greeks told stories about a war

The

with Troy. After fighting for ten years,

both sides were tired of the war. The

Greeks made a clever plan. They built an

enormous wooden horse. Their best

warriors hid inside. The Greeks wheeled

the horse to the gates of Troy and

pretended to sail away. The people of

Troy thought it was a gift.

8D

1. Read the passage aloud to your instructor.

2. Mark the **Bossy r chunks** in purple.

Bossy r Chunks

ar er ir or ur

The Greeks told stories about a war with Troy. After fighting for ten years, both sides were tired of the war. The Greeks made a clever plan. They built an enormous wooden horse. Their best warriors hid inside. The Greeks wheeled the horse to the gates of Troy and pretended to sail away. The people of Troy thought it was a gift. They wheeled the Trojan horse into their city. That was a major blunder! During the night, the Greek warriors slipped out of the Trojan horse and conquered Troy. The story of the Trojan War is still told today.

Ancient Achievements

Section 2: First Dictation

Write this week's passage from dictation. Ask for help if you need it.

The

8E

1. Read the passage aloud to your instructor.

2. Mark the **Bossy *r* chunks** in purple.

Bossy *r* Chunks

ar er ir or ur

The Greeks told stories about a war with Troy. After fighting for ten years, both sides were tired of the war. The Greeks made a clever plan. They built an enormous wooden horse. Their best warriors hid inside. The Greeks wheeled the horse to the gates of Troy and pretended to sail away. The people of Troy thought it was a gift. They wheeled the Trojan horse into their city. That was a major blunder! During the night, the Greek warriors slipped out of the Trojan horse and conquered Troy. The story of the Trojan War is still told today.

Ancient Achievements

Section 2: Second Dictation

See if you can write this week's passage from dictation without asking for help.

1. Read the passage aloud to your instructor.

2. Mark **vowel chunks** in yellow, <u>**consonant chunks**</u> in blue, and <u>**Bossy *r* chunks**</u> in purple.

Vowel Chunks	Consonant Chunks	Bossy *r*
aa ae ai ao au aw ay	ch gh sh ph th wh	ar
ea ee ei eo eu ew ey eau	wr gn kn dg qu ck	er
ia ie ii io iu	tch bb cc dd ff gg	ir
oa oe oi oo ou ow oy	hh kk ll mm nn pp	or
ua ue ui uo uu uy	rr ss tt ww vv zz	ur

The Phoenicians lived near the sea. They built sturdy ships and sailed around the ancient world trading goods. Their ships carried olive oil and cedar wood to other ports. They sold purple dye and metalwork. As they sailed, they spread their alphabet. It used letters instead of pictures. The Greeks borrowed the alphabet and made some changes. The Romans changed it even more. A few letters in our alphabet still remind us of these older letters.

Copy and chunk the passage. Look at the opposite page if you need help.

The Phoenicians lived near the sea. They

The

built sturdy ships and sailed around the

ancient world trading goods. Their ships

carried olive oil and cedar wood to

other ports. They sold purple dye and

metalwork. As they sailed, they spread

their alphabet. It used letters instead

of pictures. The Greeks borrowed the

alphabet and made some changes.

1. Read the passage aloud to your instructor.

2. Mark **<u>vowel chunks</u>** in yellow, **<u>consonant chunks</u>** in blue, and **<u>Bossy *r* chunks</u>** in purple.

Vowel Chunks	Consonant Chunks	Bossy *r*
aa ae ai ao au aw ay	ch gh sh ph th wh	ar
ea ee ei eo eu ew ey eau	wr gn kn dg qu ck	er
ia ie ii io iu	tch bb cc dd ff gg	ir
oa oe oi oo ou ow oy	hh kk ll mm nn pp	or
ua ue ui uo uu uy	rr ss tt ww vv zz	ur

The Phoenicians lived near the sea. They built sturdy ships and sailed around the ancient world trading goods. Their ships carried olive oil and cedar wood to other ports. They sold purple dye and metalwork. As they sailed, they spread their alphabet. It used letters instead of pictures. The Greeks borrowed the alphabet and made some changes. The Romans changed it even more. A few letters in our alphabet still remind us of these older letters.

Copy and chunk the passage. Look at the opposite page if you need help.

Their ships carried olive oil and cedar

Their

wood to other ports. They sold purple

dye and metalwork. As they sailed, they

spread their alphabet. It used letters

instead of pictures. The Greeks borrowed

the alphabet and made some changes.

The Romans changed it even more.

A few letters in our alphabet still remind

us of these older letters.

9C

Section 1: Vowel, Consonant, and Bossy r Chunks

1. Read the passage aloud to your instructor.

2. Mark **vowel chunks** in yellow, **consonant chunks** in blue, and **Bossy r chunks** in purple.

3. Read the Spotlight. Do the matching activity in the *Handbook* if you wish.

Vowel Chunks
aa ae ai ao au aw ay
ea ee ei eo eu ew ey eau
ia ie ii io iu
oa oe oi oo ou ow oy
ua ue ui uo uu uy

Consonant Chunks
ch gh sh ph th wh
wr gn kn dg qu ck
tch bb cc dd ff gg
hh kk ll mm nn pp
rr ss tt ww vv zz

Bossy r
ar
er
ir
or
ur

The Phoenicians lived near the sea. They built sturdy ships and sailed around the ancient world trading goods. Their ships carried olive oil and cedar wood to other ports. They sold purple dye and metalwork. As they sailed, they spread their alphabet. It used letters instead of pictures. The Greeks borrowed the alphabet and made some changes. The Romans changed it even more. A few letters in our alphabet still remind us of these older letters.

SPOTLIGHT

The combination *ph* is another common consonant chunk with a special sound. There are two different words with *ph* in this lesson. Some other words with this combination are *phone, photo, phonics, symphony, phrase,* and *physical.* All of these words come from Greek words. The *ph* sound is written with the letter φ (phi) in the Greek alphabet.

Ancient Achievements

Copy and chunk the passage. Look at the opposite page if you need help.

The Phoenicians lived near the sea. They

The

built sturdy ships and sailed around the

ancient world trading goods. Their ships

carried olive oil and cedar wood to

other ports. They sold purple dye and

metalwork. As they sailed, they spread

their alphabet. It used letters instead

of pictures. The Greeks borrowed the

alphabet and made some changes.

9D

1. Read the passage aloud to your instructor.

2. Mark **vowel chunks** in yellow, **consonant chunks** in blue, and **Bossy *r* chunks** in purple.

Vowel Chunks	Consonant Chunks	Bossy *r*
aa ae ai ao au aw ay	ch gh sh ph th wh	ar
ea ee ei eo eu ew ey eau	wr gn kn dg qu ck	er
ia ie ii io iu	tch bb cc dd ff gg	ir
oa oe oi oo ou ow oy	hh kk ll mm nn pp	or
ua ue ui uo uu uy	rr ss tt ww vv zz	ur

The Phoenicians lived near the sea. They built sturdy ships and sailed around the ancient world trading goods. Their ships carried olive oil and cedar wood to other ports. They sold purple dye and metalwork. As they sailed, they spread their alphabet. It used letters instead of pictures. The Greeks borrowed the alphabet and made some changes. The Romans changed it even more. A few letters in our alphabet still remind us of these older letters.

Section 2: First Dictation

Write this week's passage from dictation. Ask for help if you need it.

The

1. Read the passage aloud to your instructor.

2. Mark **vowel chunks** in yellow, **consonant chunks** in blue, and **Bossy *r* chunks** in purple.

Vowel Chunks	Consonant Chunks	Bossy *r*
aa ae ai ao au aw ay	ch gh sh ph th wh	ar
ea ee ei eo eu ew ey eau	wr gn kn dg qu ck	er
ia ie ii io iu	tch bb cc dd ff gg	ir
oa oe oi oo ou ow oy	hh kk ll mm nn pp	or
ua ue ui uo uu uy	rr ss tt ww vv zz	ur

The Phoenicians lived near the sea. They built sturdy ships and sailed around the ancient world trading goods. Their ships carried olive oil and cedar wood to other ports. They sold purple dye and metalwork. As they sailed, they spread their alphabet. It used letters instead of pictures. The Greeks borrowed the alphabet and made some changes. The Romans changed it even more. A few letters in our alphabet still remind us of these older letters.

Phoenician   Greek   Latin   Modern

Ancient Achievements

Section 2: Second Dictation

See if you can write this week's passage from dictation without asking for help.

10A

Section 1: Vowel, Consonant, and Bossy *r* Chunks

1. Read the passage aloud to your instructor.

2. Mark **vowel chunks** in yellow, <u>**consonant chunks**</u> in blue, and <u>**Bossy *r* chunks**</u> in purple.

Vowel Chunks	Consonant Chunks	Bossy *r*
aa ae ai ao au aw ay	ch gh sh ph th wh	ar
ea ee ei eo eu ew ey eau	wr gn kn dg qu ck	er
ia ie ii io iu	tch bb cc dd ff gg	ir
oa oe oi oo ou ow oy	hh kk ll mm nn pp	or
ua ue ui uo uu uy	rr ss tt ww vv zz	ur

Ancient Greece was made up of city-states. People were fiercely loyal to their city-state. They were often at war with other city-states. Once a year they called a truce. Men gathered to compete in foot races. Every four years they met in Olympia for special events. These early Olympics grew to include sports such as boxing and wrestling. Later, events with horses were added. Women were allowed to compete in those events. The winners brought honor to their city-states.

Copy and chunk the passage. Look at the opposite page if you need help.

Ancient Greece was made up of

Ancient

city-states. People were fiercely loyal

to their city-state. They were often at

war with other city-states. Once a year

they called a truce. Men gathered to

compete in foot races. Every four years

they met in Olympia for special events.

These early Olympics grew to include

sports such as boxing and wrestling.

1. Read the passage aloud to your instructor.

2. Mark **vowel chunks** in yellow, **consonant chunks** in blue, and **Bossy _r_ chunks** in purple.

Vowel Chunks	Consonant Chunks	Bossy _r_
aa ae ai ao au aw ay	ch gh sh ph th wh	ar
ea ee ei eo eu ew ey eau	wr gn kn dg qu ck	er
ia ie ii io iu	tch bb cc dd ff gg	ir
oa oe oi oo ou ow oy	hh kk ll mm nn pp	or
ua ue ui uo uu uy	rr ss tt ww vv zz	ur

Ancient Greece was made up of city-states. People were fiercely loyal to their city-state. They were often at war with other city-states. Once a year they called a truce. Men gathered to compete in foot races. Every four years they met in Olympia for special events. These early Olympics grew to include sports such as boxing and wrestling. Later, events with horses were added. Women were allowed to compete in those events. The winners brought honor to their city-states.

Copy and chunk the passage. Look at the opposite page if you need help.

Once a year they called a truce. Men

Once

gathered to compete in foot races. Every

four years they met in Olympia for

special events. These early Olympics

grew to include sports such as boxing

and wrestling. Later, events with horses

were added. Women were allowed to

compete in those events. The winners

brought honor to their city-states.

10C

Section 1: Vowel, Consonant, and Bossy *r* Chunks

1. Read the passage aloud to your instructor.

2. Mark **vowel chunks** in yellow, **consonant chunks** in blue, and **Bossy *r* chunks** in purple.

3. Read the Spotlight. Do the activity in the *Handbook*, if you wish.

Vowel Chunks	Consonant Chunks	Bossy *r*
aa ae ai ao au aw ay	ch gh sh ph th wh	ar
ea ee ei eo eu ew ey eau	wr gn kn dg qu ck	er
ia ie ii io iu	tch bb cc dd ff gg	ir
oa oe oi oo ou ow oy	hh kk ll mm nn pp	or
ua ue ui uo uu uy	rr ss tt ww vv zz	ur

Ancient Greece was made up of city-states. People were fiercely loyal to their city-state. They were often at war with other city-states. Once a year they called a truce. Men gathered to compete in foot races. Every four years they met in Olympia for special events. These early Olympics grew to include sports such as boxing and wrestling. Later, events with horses were added. Women were allowed to compete in those events. The winners brought honor to their city-states.

SPOTLIGHT

A *truce* is an agreement between opponents to stop fighting for a certain length of time. The *u* reminds us that *truce* is related to *trust*, even though the vowel is pronounced differently in the two words. Another related word is *truth*. If your opponent calls a *truce*, it is very important that you can *trust* him to tell you the *truth*.

98

Ancient Achievements

Copy and chunk the passage. Look at the opposite page if you need help.

Ancient Greece was made up of

Ancient

city-states. People were fiercely loyal

to their city-state. They were often at

war with other city-states. Once a year

they called a truce. Men gathered to

compete in foot races. Every four years

they met in Olympia for special events.

These early Olympics grew to include

sports such as boxing and wrestling.

1. Read the passage aloud to your instructor.

2. Mark **<u>vowel chunks</u>** in yellow, **<u>consonant chunks</u>** in blue, and **<u>Bossy *r* chunks</u>** in purple.

Vowel Chunks	Consonant Chunks	Bossy *r*
aa ae ai ao au aw ay	ch gh sh ph th wh	ar
ea ee ei eo eu ew ey eau	wr gn kn dg qu ck	er
ia ie ii io iu	tch bb cc dd ff gg	ir
oa oe oi oo ou ow oy	hh kk ll mm nn pp	or
ua ue ui uo uu uy	rr ss tt ww vv zz	ur

Ancient Greece was made up of city-states. People were fiercely loyal to their city-state. They were often at war with other city-states. Once a year they called a truce. Men gathered to compete in foot races. Every four years they met in Olympia for special events. These early Olympics grew to include sports such as boxing and wrestling. Later, events with horses were added. Women were allowed to compete in those events. The winners brought honor to their city-states.

Section 2: First Dictation

Write this week's passage from dictation. Ask for help if you need it.

Ancient

1. Read the passage aloud to your instructor.

2. Mark <u>**vowel chunks**</u> in yellow, <u>**consonant chunks**</u> in blue, and <u>**Bossy _r_ chunks**</u> in purple.

Vowel Chunks	Consonant Chunks	Bossy _r_
aa ae ai ao au aw ay	ch gh sh ph th wh	ar
ea ee ei eo eu ew ey eau	wr gn kn dg qu ck	er
ia ie ii io iu	tch bb cc dd ff gg	ir
oa oe oi oo ou ow oy	hh kk ll mm nn pp	or
ua ue ui uo uu uy	rr ss tt ww vv zz	ur

Ancient Greece was made up of city-states. People were fiercely loyal to their city-state. They were often at war with other city-states. Once a year they called a truce. Men gathered to compete in foot races. Every four years they met in Olympia for special events. These early Olympics grew to include sports such as boxing and wrestling. Later, events with horses were added. Women were allowed to compete in those events. The winners brought honor to their city-states.

Section 2: Second Dictation

See if you can write this week's passage from dictation without asking for help.

1. Read the passage aloud to your instructor.

2. The letter *y* is usually a consonant (*year, yak*), but sometimes it is "tricky" and sounds like a vowel. There is more about Tricky *y* Guy in the *Instructor's Handbook*.

3. Find each **Tricky *y* Guy** in the passage and mark it in green.

A story from long ago tells about a king who married a woman from a far country. The woman became homesick for her own country. She missed the beauty of its green hills and mountains. The king's country was extremely hot, flat, and dry. The king decided to build his wife a garden as high as a mountain. Workers used bricks and stones to build it. They added terraces filled with soil, trees, and flowers. Storytellers called the king's gift the Hanging Gardens of Babylon. Ruins of gardens have been found in dry places.

Copy and chunk the passage. Look at the opposite page if you need help.

A story from long ago tells about a king

who married a woman from a far

country. The woman became homesick

for her own country. She missed the

beauty of its green hills and mountains.

The king's country was extremely hot,

flat, and dry. The king decided to build

his wife a garden as high as a mountain.

11B

1. Read the passage aloud to your instructor.

2. Mark each **Tricky _y_ Guy** in green.

A story from long ago tells about a king who married a woman from a far country. The woman became homesick for her own country. She missed the beauty of its green hills and mountains. The king's country was extremely hot, flat, and dry. The king decided to build his wife a garden as high as a mountain. Workers used bricks and stones to build it. They added terraces filled with soil, trees, and flowers. Storytellers called the king's gift the Hanging Gardens of Babylon. Ruins of gardens have been found in dry places.

Copy and chunk the passage. Look at the opposite page if you need help.

The king's country was extremely hot,
The

flat, and dry. The king decided to build

his wife a garden as high as a mountain.

Workers used bricks and stones to build

it. They added terraces filled with soil,

trees, and flowers. Storytellers called the

king's gift the Hanging Gardens of

Babylon. Ruins of gardens have been

found in dry places.

1. Read the passage aloud to your instructor.

2. Mark each **Tricky _y_ Guy** in green.

3. Read the Spotlight. Look in the *Instructor's Handbook* for more interesting words with the *eau* letter pattern.

A story from long ago tells about a king who married a woman from a far country. The woman became homesick for her own country. She missed the beauty of its green hills and mountains. The king's country was extremely hot, flat, and dry. The king decided to build his wife a garden as high as a mountain. Workers used bricks and stones to build it. They added terraces filled with soil, trees, and flowers. Storytellers called the king's gift the Hanging Gardens of Babylon. Ruins of gardens have been found in dry places.

SPOTLIGHT

As you might guess, the word *beauty* has French roots. Learning the *eau* vowel combination in *beauty* can help you spell related words such as *beautiful, beautify, beautifully,* and *beautician*. Notice how the *y* at the end of *beauty* changes to an *i* in these words.

Copy and chunk the passage. Look at the opposite page if you need help.

A story from long ago tells about a king

who married a woman from a far

country. The woman became homesick

for her own country. She missed the

beauty of its green hills and mountains.

The king's country was extremely hot,

flat, and dry. The king decided to build

his wife a garden as high as a mountain.

1. Read the passage aloud to your instructor.

2. Mark each **Tricky *y* Guy** in green.

A story from long ago tells about a king who married a woman from a far country. The woman became homesick for her own country. She missed the beauty of its green hills and mountains. The king's country was extremely hot, flat, and dry. The king decided to build his wife a garden as high as a mountain. Workers used bricks and stones to build it. They added terraces filled with soil, trees, and flowers. Storytellers called the king's gift the Hanging Gardens of Babylon. Ruins of gardens have been found in dry places.

Section 2: First Dictation

Write this week's passage from dictation. Ask for help if you need it.

A

1. Read the passage aloud to your instructor.

2. Mark each **Tricky *y* Guy** in green.

A story from long ago tells about a king who married a woman from a far country. The woman became homesick for her own country. She missed the beauty of its green hills and mountains. The king's country was extremely hot, flat, and dry. The king decided to build his wife a garden as high as a mountain. Workers used bricks and stones to build it. They added terraces filled with soil, trees, and flowers. Storytellers called the king's gift the Hanging Gardens of Babylon. Ruins of gardens have been found in dry places.

Section 2: Second Dictation

See if you can write this week's passage from dictation without asking for help.

1. Read the passage aloud to your instructor.

2. You will be looking for five common word endings in this week's lesson.

3. Look for **endings** that are on the list and mark them in pink or red.

Endings

-ed -es -ful -ing -ly

China was often attacked by tribes living to the north. One king built a stone wall even before China was an empire. The first Chinese emperor forced his people to build a wall. They mixed sand, gravel, and clay. This mixture was then packed into place. Wall building continued for many centuries. The walls usually didn't stop enemies. However, they were helpful in slowing down an army. The most famous wall is called the Great Wall of China. You can still see parts of this wall winding over hills and valleys.

Copy and chunk the passage. Look at the opposite page if you need help.

China was often attacked by tribes living

China

to the north. One king built a stone wall

even before China was an empire. The

first Chinese emperor forced his people

to build a wall. They mixed sand, gravel,

and clay. This mixture was then packed

into place. Wall building continued for

many centuries. The walls usually didn't

stop enemies.

1. Read the passage aloud to your instructor.

2. Mark the **endings** in pink or red.

Endings

-ed -es -ful -ing -ly

China was often attacked by tribes living to the north. One king built a stone wall even before China was an empire. The first Chinese emperor forced his people to build a wall. They mixed sand, gravel, and clay. This mixture was then packed into place. Wall building continued for many centuries. The walls usually didn't stop enemies. However, they were helpful in slowing down an army. The most famous wall is called the Great Wall of China. You can still see parts of this wall winding over hills and valleys.

Copy and chunk the passage. Look at the opposite page if you need help.

They mixed sand, gravel, and clay. This

They

mixture was then packed into place. Wall

building continued for many centuries.

The walls usually didn't stop enemies.

However, they were helpful in slowing

down an army. The most famous wall is

called the Great Wall of China. You can

still see parts of this wall winding over

hills and valleys.

1. Read the passage aloud to your instructor.

2. Mark the **endings** in pink or red.

3. Read the Spotlight. Look in the *Handbook* for more about adding an *-ed* ending to different words.

Endings

-ed -es -ful -ing -ly

China was often attacked by tribes living to the north. One king built a stone wall even before China was an empire. The first Chinese emperor forced his people to build a wall. They mixed sand, gravel, and clay. This mixture was then packed into place. Wall building continued for many centuries. The walls usually didn't stop enemies. However, they were helpful in slowing down an army. The most famous wall is called the Great Wall of China. You can still see parts of this wall winding over hills and valleys.

SPOTLIGHT

The *-ed* ending added to a verb tells us that something happened in the past. Be careful when adding *-ed,* though, or you may end up with misspelled words. There are six different words in this week's passage that have *-ed* endings. Can you see how two of them were changed before the *-ed* ending was added?

Copy and chunk the passage. Look at the opposite page if you need help.

China was often attacked by tribes living

China

to the north. One king built a stone wall

even before China was an empire. The

first Chinese emperor forced his people

to build a wall. They mixed sand, gravel,

and clay. This mixture was then packed

into place. Wall building continued for

many centuries. The walls usually didn't

stop enemies.

1. Read the passage aloud to your instructor.

2. Mark the **endings** in pink or red.

Endings

-ed -es -ful -ing -ly

China was often attacked by tribes living to the north. One king built a stone wall even before China was an empire. The first Chinese emperor forced his people to build a wall. They mixed sand, gravel, and clay. This mixture was then packed into place. Wall building continued for many centuries. The walls usually didn't stop enemies. However, they were helpful in slowing down an army. The most famous wall is called the Great Wall of China. You can still see parts of this wall winding over hills and valleys.

Section 2: First Dictation

Write this week's passage from dictation. Ask for help if you need it.

China

1. Read the passage aloud to your instructor.

2. Mark the **endings** in pink or red.

Endings

-ed -es -ful -ing -ly

China was often attacked by tribes living to the north. One king built a stone wall even before China was an empire. The first Chinese emperor forced his people to build a wall. They mixed sand, gravel, and clay. This mixture was then packed into place. Wall building continued for many centuries. The walls usually didn't stop enemies. However, they were helpful in slowing down an army. The most famous wall is called the Great Wall of China. You can still see parts of this wall winding over hills and valleys.

Section 2: Second Dictation

See if you can write this week's passage from dictation without asking for help.

1. Read the passage aloud to your instructor.

2. In this lesson, you will be marking silent letters that are not part of endings or other chunks. There is more about silent letters in the *Instructor's Handbook*.

3. Look for **silent letters** and mark them in orange.

Lighthouses have guided ships for centuries. One famous lighthouse was built at Alexandria, Egypt. It was about 400 feet high. Its purpose was to help ships find the harbor. What type of light shone in this lighthouse thousands of years ago? Fire! Light from this fire guided ships at night. Some people wrote that smoke could be seen during the day. Others believe that a huge mirror reflected the sun during the day. This lighthouse was a beacon to ships and a symbol of Alexandria.

Copy and chunk the passage. Look at the opposite page if you need help.

Lighthouses have guided ships for

Lighthouses

centuries. One famous lighthouse was

built at Alexandria, Egypt. It was about

400 feet high. Its purpose was to help

ships find the harbor. What type of light

shone in this lighthouse thousands of

years ago? Fire! Light from this fire

guided ships at night. Some people wrote

that smoke could be seen during the day.

1. Read the passage aloud to your instructor.

2. Mark the **silent letters** in orange.

Lighthouses have guided ships for centuries. One famous lighthouse was built at Alexandria, Egypt. It was about 400 feet high. Its purpose was to help ships find the harbor. What type of light shone in this lighthouse thousands of years ago? Fire! Light from this fire guided ships at night. Some people wrote that smoke could be seen during the day. Others believe that a huge mirror reflected the sun during the day. This lighthouse was a beacon to ships and a symbol of Alexandria.

Copy and chunk the passage. Look at the opposite page if you need help.

Its purpose was to help ships find the

Its

harbor. What type of light shone in this

lighthouse thousands of years ago? Fire!

Light from this fire guided ships at night.

Some people wrote that smoke could be

seen during the day. Others believe that

a huge mirror reflected the sun during

the day. This lighthouse was a beacon to

ships and a symbol of Alexandria.

1. Read the passage aloud to your instructor.

2. Mark the <u>**silent letters**</u> in orange.

3. Read the Spotlight.

Lighthouses have guided ships for centuries. One famous lighthouse was built at Alexandria, Egypt. It was about 400 feet high. Its purpose was to help ships find the harbor. What type of light shone in this lighthouse thousands of years ago? Fire! Light from this fire guided ships at night. Some people wrote that smoke could be seen during the day. Others believe that a huge mirror reflected the sun during the day. This lighthouse was a beacon to ships and a symbol of Alexandria.

SPOTLIGHT

Take a look at the compound word *lighthouse.* Can you think of other compound words that end with the word *house? Farmhouse* is one example. Although there are many compound words ending with *house,* compound words beginning with *light* are uncommon. Two of them are *lightweight* and *lightship.* Most phrases beginning with *light* are written as two separate words. (Example: *light show*)

Copy and chunk the passage. Look at the opposite page if you need help.

Lighthouses have guided ships for

Lighthouses

centuries. One famous lighthouse was

built at Alexandria, Egypt. It was about

400 feet high. Its purpose was to help

ships find the harbor. What type of light

shone in this lighthouse thousands of

years ago? Fire! Light from this fire

guided ships at night. Some people wrote

that smoke could be seen during the day.

1. Read the passage aloud to your instructor.

2. Mark the **silent letters** in orange.

Lighthouses have guided ships for centuries. One famous lighthouse was built at Alexandria, Egypt. It was about 400 feet high. Its purpose was to help ships find the harbor. What type of light shone in this lighthouse thousands of years ago? Fire! Light from this fire guided ships at night. Some people wrote that smoke could be seen during the day. Others believe that a huge mirror reflected the sun during the day. This lighthouse was a beacon to ships and a symbol of Alexandria.

Write this week's passage from dictation. Ask for help if you need it.

Lighthouses

1. Read the passage aloud to your instructor.

2. Mark the <u>**silent letters**</u> in orange.

Lighthouses have guided ships for centuries. One famous lighthouse was built at Alexandria, Egypt. It was about 400 feet high. Its purpose was to help ships find the harbor. What type of light shone in this lighthouse thousands of years ago? Fire! Light from this fire guided ships at night. Some people wrote that smoke could be seen during the day. Others believe that a huge mirror reflected the sun during the day. This lighthouse was a beacon to ships and a symbol of Alexandria.

Section 2: Second Dictation

See if you can write this week's passage from dictation without asking for help.

1. Read the passage aloud to your instructor.

2. This week you will be marking all six letter patterns that you have learned. They are **vowel chunks** (yellow), **consonant chunks** (blue), **Bossy _r_ chunks** (purple), **Tricky _y_ Guy** (green), **endings** (pink or red), and **silent letters** (orange).

Vowel Chunks	Consonant Chunks	Bossy _r_	Endings
aa ae ai ao au aw ay	ch gh sh ph th wh	ar	-ed
ea ee ei eo eu ew ey eau	wr gn kn dg qu ck	er	-es
ia ie ii io iu	tch bb cc dd ff gg	ir	-ful
oa oe oi oo ou ow oy	hh kk ll mm nn pp	or	-ing
ua ue ui uo uu uy	rr ss tt ww vv zz	ur	-ly

Thousands of years ago, the people of Athens tried something new. They didn't want to be ruled by one person or family. They created a new form of government. Citizens met often to discuss and debate. They made the laws. They also served in office. Only free men over 18 were citizens. Our word democracy comes from two Greek words. _Demos_ means the common people of a country. _Kratos_ means rule. In a democracy, the people rule.

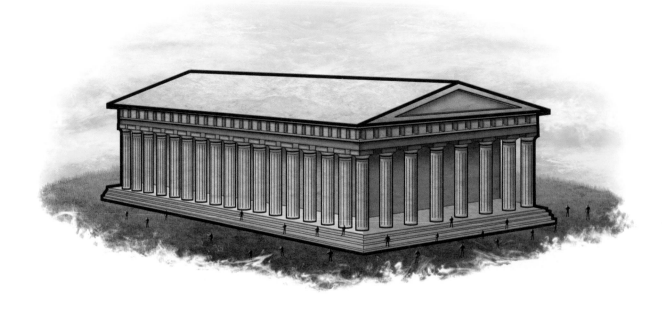

Copy and chunk the passage. Look at the opposite page if you need help.

Thousands of years ago, the people of

Thousands

Athens tried something new. They didn't

want to be ruled by one person or family.

They created a new form of government.

Citizens met often to discuss and debate.

They made the laws. They also served in

office. Only free men over 18 were

citizens. Our word democracy comes

from two Greek words.

1. Read the passage aloud to your instructor.

2. Mark all six letter patterns that you have learned. They are **vowel chunks** (yellow), **consonant chunks** (blue), **Bossy *r* chunks** (purple), **Tricky *y* Guy** (green), **endings** (pink or red), and **silent letters** (orange).

Vowel Chunks	Consonant Chunks	Bossy *r*	Endings
aa ae ai ao au aw ay	ch gh sh ph th wh	ar	-ed
ea ee ei eo eu ew ey eau	wr gn kn dg qu ck	er	-es
ia ie ii io iu	tch bb cc dd ff gg	ir	-ful
oa oe oi oo ou ow oy	hh kk ll mm nn pp	or	-ing
ua ue ui uo uu uy	rr ss tt ww vv zz	ur	-ly

Thousands of years ago, the people of Athens tried something new. They didn't want to be ruled by one person or family. They created a new form of government. Citizens met often to discuss and debate. They made the laws. They also served in office. Only free men over 18 were citizens. Our word democracy comes from two Greek words. *Demos* means the common people of a country. *Kratos* means rule. In a democracy, the people rule.

Copy and chunk the passage. Look at the opposite page if you need help.

They created a new form of government.

They

Citizens met often to discuss and debate.

They made the laws. They also served in

office. Only free men over 18 were

citizens. Our word democracy comes

from two Greek words. <u>Demos</u> means

the common people of a country.

<u>Kratos</u> means rule. In a democracy, the

people rule.

1. Read the passage aloud to your instructor.

2. Mark all six letter patterns that you have learned. They are **vowel chunks** (yellow), **consonant chunks** (blue), **Bossy _r_ chunks** (purple), **Tricky _y_ Guy** (green), **endings** (pink or red), and **silent letters** (orange).

3. Read the Spotlight.

Vowel Chunks	Consonant Chunks	Bossy _r_	Endings
aa ae ai ao au aw ay	ch gh sh ph th wh	ar	-ed
ea ee ei eo eu ew ey eau	wr gn kn dg qu ck	er	-es
ia ie ii io iu	tch bb cc dd ff gg	ir	-ful
oa oe oi oo ou ow oy	hh kk ll mm nn pp	or	-ing
ua ue ui uo uu uy	rr ss tt ww vv zz	ur	-ly

Thousands of years ago, the people of Athens tried something new. They didn't want to be ruled by one person or family. They created a new form of government. Citizens met often to discuss and debate. They made the laws. They also served in office. Only free men over 18 were citizens. Our word democracy comes from two Greek words. _Demos_ means the common people of a country. _Kratos_ means rule. In a democracy, the people rule.

SPOTLIGHT

The first meaning of _citizen_ was "someone who lives in a city." The word _civil_ comes from a Latin word that meant "related to a citizen." To be _civil_ or _civilized_ is to know how to behave in the city (or anywhere else). _Civics_ is the study of the duty of a citizen. _Civil law_ is law related to the life of the city. _Civilians_ are not soldiers. In other words, they are free to participate in the life of the city.

Copy and chunk the passage. Look at the opposite page if you need help.

Thousands of years ago, the people of

Thousands

Athens tried something new. They didn't

want to be ruled by one person or family.

They created a new form of government.

Citizens met often to discuss and debate.

They made the laws. They also served in

office. Only free men over 18 were

citizens. Our word democracy comes

from two Greek words.

1. Read the passage aloud to your instructor.

2. Mark all six letter patterns that you have learned. They are <u>vowel chunks</u> (yellow), <u>consonant chunks</u> (blue), <u>Bossy *r* chunks</u> (purple), <u>Tricky *y* Guy</u> (green), <u>endings</u> (pink or red), and <u>silent letters</u> (orange).

Vowel Chunks		Consonant Chunks		Bossy *r*	Endings
aa ae ai ao au aw ay		ch gh sh ph th wh		ar	-ed
ea ee ei eo eu ew ey eau		wr gn kn dg qu ck		er	-es
ia ie ii io iu		tch bb cc dd ff gg		ir	-ful
oa oe oi oo ou ow oy		hh kk ll mm nn pp		or	-ing
ua ue ui uo uu uy		rr ss tt ww vv zz		ur	-ly

Thousands of years ago, the people of Athens tried something new. They didn't want to be ruled by one person or family. They created a new form of government. Citizens met often to discuss and debate. They made the laws. They also served in office. Only free men over 18 were citizens. Our word democracy comes from two Greek words. *Demos* means the common people of a country. *Kratos* means rule. In a democracy, the people rule.

Write this week's passage from dictation. Ask for help if you need it.

Thousands

1. Read the passage aloud to your instructor.

2. Mark all six letter patterns that you have learned. They are <u>vowel chunks</u> (yellow), <u>consonant chunks</u> (blue), <u>Bossy *r* chunks</u> (purple), <u>Tricky *y* Guy</u> (green), <u>endings</u> (pink or red), and <u>silent letters</u> (orange).

Vowel Chunks	Consonant Chunks	Bossy *r*	Endings
aa ae ai ao au aw ay	ch gh sh ph th wh	ar	-ed
ea ee ei eo eu ew ey eau	wr gn kn dg qu ck	er	-es
ia ie ii io iu	tch bb cc dd ff gg	ir	-ful
oa oe oi oo ou ow oy	hh kk ll mm nn pp	or	-ing
ua ue ui uo uu uy	rr ss tt ww vv zz	ur	-ly

Thousands of years ago, the people of Athens tried something new. They didn't want to be ruled by one person or family. They created a new form of government. Citizens met often to discuss and debate. They made the laws. They also served in office. Only free men over 18 were citizens. Our word democracy comes from two Greek words. *Demos* means the common people of a country. *Kratos* means rule. In a democracy, the people rule.

demos   kratos   democracy

See if you can write this week's passage from dictation without asking for help.

15A

Section 1: All Letter Patterns

1. Read the passage aloud to your instructor.

2. Mark all six letter patterns that you have learned. They are **vowel chunks** (yellow), **consonant chunks** (blue), **Bossy *r* chunks** (purple), **Tricky *y* Guy** (green), **endings** (pink or red), and **silent letters** (orange).

Vowel Chunks	Consonant Chunks	Bossy *r*	Endings
aa ae ai ao au aw ay	ch gh sh ph th wh	ar	-ed
ea ee ei eo eu ew ey eau	wr gn kn dg qu ck	er	-es
ia ie ii io iu	tch bb cc dd ff gg	ir	-ful
oa oe oi oo ou ow oy	hh kk ll mm nn pp	or	-ing
ua ue ui uo uu uy	rr ss tt ww vv zz	ur	-ly

Chariot races were popular in ancient Greece. Horses burst from the starting gates. Men standing in chariots whipped their horses fiercely. The frenzy began! Fans cheered wildly for their favorite teams. Hooves thundered. Whips cracked. Dust rose thickly from the racetrack. At the turns, chariots often crashed into each other or into the side walls. Sometimes teams ran over the wrecked chariots. This kind of racing was a very risky sport!

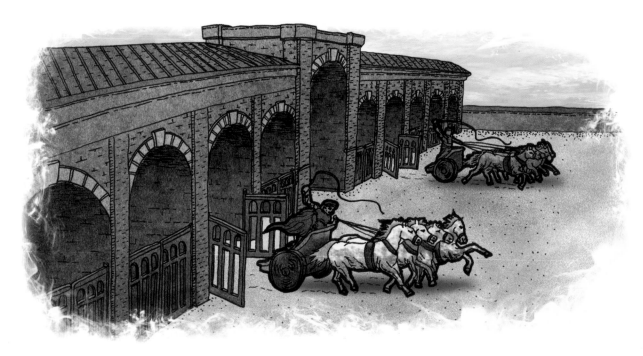

Ancient Achievements

Copy and chunk the passage. Look at the opposite page if you need help.

Chariot races were popular in ancient
Chariot

Greece. Horses burst from the starting

gates. Men standing in chariots whipped

their horses fiercely. The frenzy began!

Fans cheered wildly for their favorite

teams. Hooves thundered. Whips

cracked. Dust rose thickly from the

racetrack. At the turns, chariots often

crashed into each other.

15B

1. Read the passage aloud to your instructor.

2. Mark all six letter patterns that you have learned. They are **vowel chunks** (yellow), **consonant chunks** (blue), **Bossy _r_ chunks** (purple), **Tricky _y_ Guy** (green), **endings** (pink or red), and **silent letters** (orange).

Vowel Chunks								Consonant Chunks						Bossy _r_	Endings
aa	ae	ai	ao	au	aw	ay		ch	gh	sh	ph	th	wh	ar	-ed
ea	ee	ei	eo	eu	ew	ey	eau	wr	gn	kn	dg	qu	ck	er	-es
ia	ie	ii	io	iu				tch	bb	cc	dd	ff	gg	ir	-ful
oa	oe	oi	oo	ou	ow	oy		hh	kk	ll	mm	nn	pp	or	-ing
ua	ue	ui	uo	uu	uy			rr	ss	tt	ww	vv	zz	ur	-ly

Chariot races were popular in ancient Greece. Horses burst from the starting gates. Men standing in chariots whipped their horses fiercely. The frenzy began! Fans cheered wildly for their favorite teams. Hooves thundered. Whips cracked. Dust rose thickly from the racetrack. At the turns, chariots often crashed into each other or into the side walls. Sometimes teams ran over the wrecked chariots. This kind of racing was a very risky sport!

Ancient Achievements

Copy and chunk the passage. Look at the opposite page if you need help.

The frenzy began! Fans cheered wildly
The

for their favorite teams. Hooves

thundered. Whips cracked. Dust rose

thickly from the racetrack. At the turns,

chariots often crashed into each other

or into the side walls. Sometimes teams

ran over the wrecked chariots. This kind

of racing was a very risky sport!

1. Read the passage aloud to your instructor.

2. Mark all six letter patterns that you have learned. They are **vowel chunks** (yellow), **consonant chunks** (blue), **Bossy _r_ chunks** (purple), **Tricky _y_ Guy** (green), **endings** (pink or red), and **silent letters** (orange).

3. Read the Spotlight. Go to the *Instructor's Handbook* for more compound words that begin with *some* or end with *time*.

Vowel Chunks								Consonant Chunks						Bossy _r_	Endings
aa	ae	ai	ao	au	aw	ay		ch	gh	sh	ph	th	wh	ar	-ed
ea	ee	ei	eo	eu	ew	ey	eau	wr	gn	kn	dg	qu	ck	er	-es
ia	ie	ii	io	iu				tch	bb	cc	dd	ff	gg	ir	-ful
oa	oe	oi	oo	ou	ow	oy		hh	kk	ll	mm	nn	pp	or	-ing
ua	ue	ui	uo	uu	uy			rr	ss	tt	ww	vv	zz	ur	-ly

Chariot races were popular in ancient Greece. Horses burst from the starting gates. Men standing in chariots whipped their horses fiercely. The frenzy began! Fans cheered wildly for their favorite teams. Hooves thundered. Whips cracked. Dust rose thickly from the racetrack. At the turns, chariots often crashed into each other or into the side walls. Sometimes teams ran over the wrecked chariots. This kind of racing was a very risky sport!

SPOTLIGHT

In this passage, you will find the compound word *sometimes.* Can you think of other compound words that begin with *some* or end with *time*? Be careful! Sometimes two separate words work together to name one thing. For example, *story time* is written as two words, but together the words describe one idea.

Copy and chunk the passage. Look at the opposite page if you need help.

Chariot races were popular in ancient

Chariot

Greece. Horses burst from the starting

gates. Men standing in chariots whipped

their horses fiercely. The frenzy began!

Fans cheered wildly for their favorite

teams. Hooves thundered. Whips

cracked. Dust rose thickly from the

racetrack. At the turns, chariots often

crashed into each other.

1. Read the passage aloud to your instructor.

2. Mark all six letter patterns that you have learned. They are **vowel chunks** (yellow), **consonant chunks** (blue), **Bossy *r* chunks** (purple), **Tricky *y* Guy** (green), **endings** (pink or red), and **silent letters** (orange).

Vowel Chunks	Consonant Chunks	Bossy *r*	Endings
aa ae ai ao au aw ay	ch gh sh ph th wh	ar	-ed
ea ee ei eo eu ew ey eau	wr gn kn dg qu ck	er	-es
ia ie ii io iu	tch bb cc dd ff gg	ir	-ful
oa oe oi oo ou ow oy	hh kk ll mm nn pp	or	-ing
ua ue ui uo uu uy	rr ss tt ww vv zz	ur	-ly

Chariot races were popular in ancient Greece. Horses burst from the starting gates. Men standing in chariots whipped their horses fiercely. The frenzy began! Fans cheered wildly for their favorite teams. Hooves thundered. Whips cracked. Dust rose thickly from the racetrack. At the turns, chariots often crashed into each other or into the side walls. Sometimes teams ran over the wrecked chariots. This kind of racing was a very risky sport!

Write this week's passage from dictation. Ask for help if you need it.

Chariot

1. Read the passage aloud to your instructor.

2. Mark all six letter patterns that you have learned. They are **vowel chunks** (yellow), **consonant chunks** (blue), **Bossy _r_ chunks** (purple), **Tricky _y_ Guy** (green), **endings** (pink or red), and **silent letters** (orange).

Vowel Chunks	Consonant Chunks	Bossy _r_	Endings
aa ae ai ao au aw ay	ch gh sh ph th wh	ar	-ed
ea ee ei eo eu ew ey eau	wr gn kn dg qu ck	er	-es
ia ie ii io iu	tch bb cc dd ff gg	ir	-ful
oa oe oi oo ou ow oy	hh kk ll mm nn pp	or	-ing
ua ue ui uo uu uy	rr ss tt ww vv zz	ur	-ly

Chariot races were popular in ancient Greece. Horses burst from the starting gates. Men standing in chariots whipped their horses fiercely. The frenzy began! Fans cheered wildly for their favorite teams. Hooves thundered. Whips cracked. Dust rose thickly from the racetrack. At the turns, chariots often crashed into each other or into the side walls. Sometimes teams ran over the wrecked chariots. This kind of racing was a very risky sport!

Section 2: Second Dictation

See if you can write this week's passage from dictation without asking for help.

1. Read the passage aloud to your instructor.

2. Mark all six letter patterns that you have learned. They are **vowel chunks** (yellow), **consonant chunks** (blue), **Bossy *r* chunks** (purple), **Tricky *y* Guy** (green), **endings** (pink or red), and **silent letters** (orange).

Vowel Chunks	Consonant Chunks	Bossy *r*	Endings
aa ae ai ao au aw ay	ch gh sh ph th wh	ar	-ed
ea ee ei eo eu ew ey eau	wr gn kn dg qu ck	er	-es
ia ie ii io iu	tch bb cc dd ff gg	ir	-ful
oa oe oi oo ou ow oy	hh kk ll mm nn pp	or	-ing
ua ue ui uo uu uy	rr ss tt ww vv zz	ur	-ly

The Roman Empire grew in size and power over many centuries. It's no wonder! Its large army was a fighting machine. Soldiers were well trained and well organized. As they conquered more and more people, they acquired more and more land. The army built a system of roads throughout the vast empire. This helped soldiers travel quickly. They preferred to build straight roads. After all, marching around curves took more time! Roman roads were well built. Some of them lasted longer than the Empire.

Copy and chunk the passage. Look at the opposite page if you need help.

The Roman Empire grew in size and
The

power over many centuries. It's no

wonder! Its large army was a fighting

machine. Soldiers were well trained and

well organized. As they conquered more

and more people, they acquired more

and more land. The army built a system

of roads throughout the vast empire.

This helped soldiers travel quickly.

1. Read the passage aloud to your instructor.

2. Mark all six letter patterns that you have learned. They are <u>**vowel chunks**</u> (yellow), <u>**consonant chunks**</u> (blue), <u>**Bossy *r* chunks**</u> (purple), <u>**Tricky *y* Guy**</u> (green), <u>**endings**</u> (pink or red), and <u>**silent letters**</u> (orange).

Vowel Chunks								Consonant Chunks						Bossy *r*	Endings
aa	ae	ai	ao	au	aw	ay		ch	gh	sh	ph	th	wh	ar	-ed
ea	ee	ei	eo	eu	ew	ey	eau	wr	gn	kn	dg	qu	ck	er	-es
ia	ie	ii	io	iu				tch	bb	cc	dd	ff	gg	ir	-ful
oa	oe	oi	oo	ou	ow	oy		hh	kk	ll	mm	nn	pp	or	-ing
ua	ue	ui	uo	uu	uy			rr	ss	tt	ww	vv	zz	ur	-ly

The Roman Empire grew in size and power over many centuries. It's no wonder! Its large army was a fighting machine. Soldiers were well trained and well organized. As they conquered more and more people, they acquired more and more land. The army built a system of roads throughout the vast empire. This helped soldiers travel quickly. They preferred to build straight roads. After all, marching around curves took more time! Roman roads were well built. Some of them lasted longer than the Empire.

Copy and chunk the passage. Look at the opposite page if you need help.

As they conquered more and more

As

people, they acquired more and more

land. The army built a system of roads

throughout the vast empire. This helped

soldiers travel quickly. They preferred to

build straight roads. After all, marching

around curves took more time! Roman

roads were well built. Some of them

lasted longer than the Empire.

1. Read the passage aloud to your instructor.

2. Mark all six letter patterns that you have learned. They are **vowel chunks** (yellow), **consonant chunks** (blue), **Bossy *r* chunks** (purple), **Tricky *y* Guy** (green), **endings** (pink or red), and **silent letters** (orange).

3. Read the Spotlight.

Vowel Chunks	Consonant Chunks	Bossy *r*	Endings
aa ae ai ao au aw ay	ch gh sh ph th wh	ar	-ed
ea ee ei eo eu ew ey eau	wr gn kn dg qu ck	er	-es
ia ie ii io iu	tch bb cc dd ff gg	ir	-ful
oa oe oi oo ou ow oy	hh kk ll mm nn pp	or	-ing
ua ue ui uo uu uy	rr ss tt ww vv zz	ur	-ly

The Roman Empire grew in size and power over many centuries. It's no wonder! Its large army was a fighting machine. Soldiers were well trained and well organized. As they conquered more and more people, they acquired more and more land. The army built a system of roads throughout the vast empire. This helped soldiers travel quickly. They preferred to build straight roads. After all, marching around curves took more time! Roman roads were well built. Some of them lasted longer than the Empire.

SPOTLIGHT

How many words can you think of that rhyme with *built?* There are many one-syllable words that have the same middle and ending sounds as *built.* Surprisingly, only two (besides *built*) have the *uilt* letter pattern. The others all have *ilt,* as in *kilt.* There are lists of both groups of words in the *Instructor's Handbook.*

Copy and chunk the passage. Look at the opposite page if you need help.

The Roman Empire grew in size and

The

power over many centuries. It's no

wonder! Its large army was a fighting

machine. Soldiers were well trained and

well organized. As they conquered more

and more people, they acquired more

and more land. The army built a system

of roads throughout the vast empire.

This helped soldiers travel quickly.

1. Read the passage aloud to your instructor.

2. Mark all six letter patterns that you have learned. They are <u>**vowel chunks**</u> (yellow), <u>**consonant chunks**</u> (blue), <u>**Bossy *r* chunks**</u> (purple), <u>**Tricky *y* Guy**</u> (green), <u>**endings**</u> (pink or red), and <u>**silent letters**</u> (orange).

Vowel Chunks								Consonant Chunks						Bossy *r*	Endings
aa	ae	ai	ao	au	aw	ay		ch	gh	sh	ph	th	wh	ar	-ed
ea	ee	ei	eo	eu	ew	ey	eau	wr	gn	kn	dg	qu	ck	er	-es
ia	ie	ii	io	iu				tch	bb	cc	dd	ff	gg	ir	-ful
oa	oe	oi	oo	ou	ow	oy		hh	kk	ll	mm	nn	pp	or	-ing
ua	ue	ui	uo	uu	uy			rr	ss	tt	ww	vv	zz	ur	-ly

The Roman Empire grew in size and power over many centuries. It's no wonder! Its large army was a fighting machine. Soldiers were well trained and well organized. As they conquered more and more people, they acquired more and more land. The army built a system of roads throughout the vast empire. This helped soldiers travel quickly. They preferred to build straight roads. After all, marching around curves took more time! Roman roads were well built. Some of them lasted longer than the Empire.

Section 2: First Dictation

Write this week's passage from dictation. Ask for help if you need it.

The

1. Read the passage aloud to your instructor.

2. Mark all six letter patterns that you have learned. They are **vowel chunks** (yellow), **consonant chunks** (blue), **Bossy *r* chunks** (purple), **Tricky *y* Guy** (green), **endings** (pink or red), and **silent letters** (orange).

Vowel Chunks	Consonant Chunks	Bossy *r*	Endings
aa ae ai ao au aw ay	ch gh sh ph th wh	ar	-ed
ea ee ei eo eu ew ey eau	wr gn kn dg qu ck	er	-es
ia ie ii io iu	tch bb cc dd ff gg	ir	-ful
oa oe oi oo ou ow oy	hh kk ll mm nn pp	or	-ing
ua ue ui uo uu uy	rr ss tt ww vv zz	ur	-ly

The Roman Empire grew in size and power over many centuries. It's no wonder! Its large army was a fighting machine. Soldiers were well trained and well organized. As they conquered more and more people, they acquired more and more land. The army built a system of roads throughout the vast empire. This helped soldiers travel quickly. They preferred to build straight roads. After all, marching around curves took more time! Roman roads were well built. Some of them lasted longer than the Empire.

Section 2: Second Dictation

See if you can write this week's passage from dictation without asking for help.

1. Read the passage aloud to your instructor.

2. Mark all six letter patterns that you have learned. They are **vowel chunks** (yellow), **consonant chunks** (blue), **Bossy *r* chunks** (purple), **Tricky *y* Guy** (green), **endings** (pink or red), and **silent letters** (orange).

Vowel Chunks	Consonant Chunks	Bossy *r*	Endings
aa ae ai ao au aw ay	ch gh sh ph th wh	ar	-ed
ea ee ei eo eu ew ey eau	wr gn kn dg qu ck	er	-es
ia ie ii io iu	tch bb cc dd ff gg	ir	-ful
oa oe oi oo ou ow oy	hh kk ll mm nn pp	or	-ing
ua ue ui uo uu uy	rr ss tt ww vv zz	ur	-ly

Two thousand years ago in the Philippines, some people faced a challenge. How could they farm the steep mountainsides where they lived? They planned and worked. They built walls of mud and stone. They created terraces along the sides of the mountains. A system of bamboo pipes was used to carry water down from the forest on top of the mountain. At first they grew a plant called taro. Later, each terrace became a rice paddy. With vision and hard work, they met the challenge of the mountain.

Copy and chunk the passage. Look at the opposite page if you need help.

Two thousand years ago in the

Two

Philippines, some people faced a

challenge. How could they farm the

steep mountainsides where they lived?

They planned and worked. They built

walls of mud and stone. They created

terraces along the sides of the

mountains. A system of bamboo pipes

was used to carry water.

1. Read the passage aloud to your instructor.

2. Mark all six letter patterns that you have learned. They are **vowel chunks** (yellow), **consonant chunks** (blue), **Bossy *r* chunks** (purple), **Tricky *y* Guy** (green), **endings** (pink or red), and **silent letters** (orange).

Vowel Chunks	Consonant Chunks	Bossy *r*	Endings
aa ae ai ao au aw ay	ch gh sh ph th wh	ar	-ed
ea ee ei eo eu ew ey eau	wr gn kn dg qu ck	er	-es
ia ie ii io iu	tch bb cc dd ff gg	ir	-ful
oa oe oi oo ou ow oy	hh kk ll mm nn pp	or	-ing
ua ue ui uo uu uy	rr ss tt ww vv zz	ur	-ly

Two thousand years ago in the Philippines, some people faced a challenge. How could they farm the steep mountainsides where they lived? They planned and worked. They built walls of mud and stone. They created terraces along the sides of the mountains. A system of bamboo pipes was used to carry water down from the forest on top of the mountain. At first they grew a plant called taro. Later, each terrace became a rice paddy. With vision and hard work, they met the challenge of the mountain.

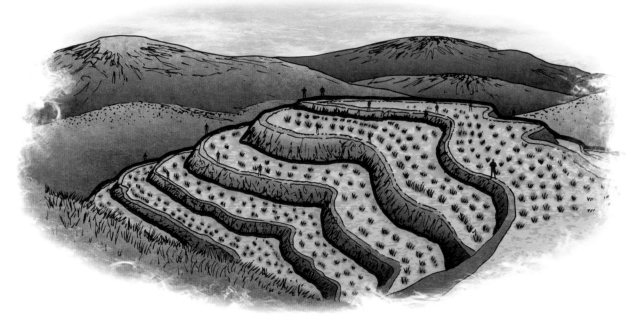

Copy and chunk the passage. Look at the opposite page if you need help.

They built walls of mud and stone. They
They

created terraces along the sides of the

mountains. A system of bamboo pipes

was used to carry water down from the

forest on top of the mountain. At first

they grew a plant called taro. Later, each

terrace became a rice paddy. With vision

and hard work, they met the challenge

of the mountain.

1. Read the passage aloud to your instructor.

2. Mark all six letter patterns that you have learned. They are **vowel chunks** (yellow), **consonant chunks** (blue), **Bossy *r* chunks** (purple), **Tricky *y* Guy** (green), **endings** (pink or red), and **silent letters** (orange).

3. Read the Spotlight. Look in the *Handbook* for more about adding an *-es* ending to different words.

Vowel Chunks	Consonant Chunks	Bossy *r*	Endings
aa ae ai ao au aw ay	ch gh sh ph th wh	ar	-ed
ea ee ei eo eu ew ey eau	wr gn kn dg qu ck	er	-es
ia ie ii io iu	tch bb cc dd ff gg	ir	-ful
oa oe oi oo ou ow oy	hh kk ll mm nn pp	or	-ing
ua ue ui uo uu uy	rr ss tt ww vv zz	ur	-ly

Two thousand years ago in the Philippines, some people faced a challenge. How could they farm the steep mountainsides where they lived? They planned and worked. They built walls of mud and stone. They created terraces along the sides of the mountains. A system of bamboo pipes was used to carry water down from the forest on top of the mountain. At first they grew a plant called taro. Later, each terrace became a rice paddy. With vision and hard work, they met the challenge of the mountain.

SPOTLIGHT

Modern English has many words that have come from Greek, Latin, Old English, and French. Did you know that some words have traveled much farther to get to us? For example, the word *bamboo* probably came from Malaysia. It was brought to Europe by Portuguese and Dutch explorers and traders who sailed to southeastern Asia in the 1500s.

Copy and chunk the passage. Look at the opposite page if you need help.

Two thousand years ago in the

Two

Philippines, some people faced a

challenge. How could they farm the

steep mountainsides where they lived?

They planned and worked. They built

walls of mud and stone. They created

terraces along the sides of the

mountains. A system of bamboo pipes

was used to carry water.

1. Read the passage aloud to your instructor.

2. Mark all six letter patterns that you have learned. They are **vowel chunks** (yellow), **consonant chunks** (blue), **Bossy *r* chunks** (purple), **Tricky *y* Guy** (green), **endings** (pink or red), and **silent letters** (orange).

Vowel Chunks	Consonant Chunks	Bossy *r*	Endings
aa ae ai ao au aw ay	ch gh sh ph th wh	ar	-ed
ea ee ei eo eu ew ey eau	wr gn kn dg qu ck	er	-es
ia ie ii io iu	tch bb cc dd ff gg	ir	-ful
oa oe oi oo ou ow oy	hh kk ll mm nn pp	or	-ing
ua ue ui uo uu uy	rr ss tt ww vv zz	ur	-ly

Two thousand years ago in the Philippines, some people faced a challenge. How could they farm the steep mountainsides where they lived? They planned and worked. They built walls of mud and stone. They created terraces along the sides of the mountains. A system of bamboo pipes was used to carry water down from the forest on top of the mountain. At first they grew a plant called taro. Later, each terrace became a rice paddy. With vision and hard work, they met the challenge of the mountain.

Section 2: First Dictation

Write this week's passage from dictation. Ask for help if you need it.

Two

1. Read the passage aloud to your instructor.

2. Mark all six letter patterns that you have learned. They are **vowel chunks** (yellow), **consonant chunks** (blue), **Bossy r chunks** (purple), **Tricky y Guy** (green), **endings** (pink or red), and **silent letters** (orange).

Vowel Chunks	Consonant Chunks	Bossy r	Endings
aa ae ai ao au aw ay	ch gh sh ph th wh	ar	-ed
ea ee ei eo eu ew ey eau	wr gn kn dg qu ck	er	-es
ia ie ii io iu	tch bb cc dd ff gg	ir	-ful
oa oe oi oo ou ow oy	hh kk ll mm nn pp	or	-ing
ua ue ui uo uu uy	rr ss tt ww vv zz	ur	-ly

Two thousand years ago in the Philippines, some people faced a challenge. How could they farm the steep mountainsides where they lived? They planned and worked. They built walls of mud and stone. They created terraces along the sides of the mountains. A system of bamboo pipes was used to carry water down from the forest on top of the mountain. At first they grew a plant called taro. Later, each terrace became a rice paddy. With vision and hard work, they met the challenge of the mountain.

taro plant   *rice plant*

Section 2: Second Dictation

See if you can write this week's passage from dictation without asking for help.

1. Read the passage aloud to your instructor.

2. Mark all six letter patterns that you have learned. They are **vowel chunks** (yellow), **consonant chunks** (blue), **Bossy *r* chunks** (purple), **Tricky *y* Guy** (green), **endings** (pink or red), and **silent letters** (orange).

Vowel Chunks	Consonant Chunks	Bossy *r*	Endings
aa ae ai ao au aw ay	ch gh sh ph th wh	ar	-ed
ea ee ei eo eu ew ey eau	wr gn kn dg qu ck	er	-es
ia ie ii io iu	tch bb cc dd ff gg	ir	-ful
oa oe oi oo ou ow oy	hh kk ll mm nn pp	or	-ing
ua ue ui uo uu uy	rr ss tt ww vv zz	ur	-ly

Some of the world's treasures have been found by accident. One example is the Dead Sea Scrolls. A young man was tending his goats near the rugged shores of the Dead Sea. He noticed one goat was missing. As he searched the rocky terrain, he entered a cave. There he found clay jars with ancient scrolls inside. The scrolls were copies of many old books. Some of them were old copies of parts of the Hebrew Bible. Scholars believe these long-lost scrolls were hidden about 1900 years before they were found.

Copy and chunk the passage. Look at the opposite page if you need help.

Some of the world's treasures have been

Some

found by accident. One example is the

Dead Sea Scrolls. A young man was

tending his goats near the rugged shores

of the Dead Sea. He noticed one goat

was missing. As he searched the rocky

terrain, he entered a cave. There he

found clay jars with ancient scrolls

inside.

1. Read the passage aloud to your instructor.

2. Mark all six letter patterns that you have learned. They are **vowel chunks** (yellow), **consonant chunks** (blue), **Bossy _r_ chunks** (purple), **Tricky _y_ Guy** (green), **endings** (pink or red), and **silent letters** (orange).

Vowel Chunks	Consonant Chunks	Bossy _r_	Endings
aa ae ai ao au aw ay	ch gh sh ph th wh	ar	-ed
ea ee ei eo eu ew ey eau	wr gn kn dg qu ck	er	-es
ia ie ii io iu	tch bb cc dd ff gg	ir	-ful
oa oe oi oo ou ow oy	hh kk ll mm nn pp	or	-ing
ua ue ui uo uu uy	rr ss tt ww vv zz	ur	-ly

Some of the world's treasures have been found by accident. One example is the Dead Sea Scrolls. A young man was tending his goats near the rugged shores of the Dead Sea. He noticed one goat was missing. As he searched the rocky terrain, he entered a cave. There he found clay jars with ancient scrolls inside. The scrolls were copies of many old books. Some of them were old copies of parts of the Hebrew Bible. Scholars believe these long-lost scrolls were hidden about 1900 years before they were found.

Copy and chunk the passage. Look at the opposite page if you need help.

He noticed one goat was missing.

He

As he searched the rocky terrain, he

entered a cave. There he found clay jars

with ancient scrolls inside. The scrolls

were copies of many old books. Some of

them were old copies of parts of the

Hebrew Bible. Scholars believe these

long-lost scrolls were hidden about 1900

years before they were found.

1. Read the passage aloud to your instructor.

2. Mark all six letter patterns that you have learned. They are **vowel chunks** (yellow), **consonant chunks** (blue), **Bossy *r* chunks** (purple), **Tricky *y* Guy** (green), **endings** (pink or red), and **silent letters** (orange).

3. Read the Spotlight.

Vowel Chunks	Consonant Chunks	Bossy *r*	Endings
aa ae ai ao au aw ay	ch gh sh ph th wh	ar	-ed
ea ee ei eo eu ew ey eau	wr gn kn dg qu ck	er	-es
ia ie ii io iu	tch bb cc dd ff gg	ir	-ful
oa oe oi oo ou ow oy	hh kk ll mm nn pp	or	-ing
ua ue ui uo uu uy	rr ss tt ww vv zz	ur	-ly

Some of the world's treasures have been found by accident. One example is the Dead Sea Scrolls. A young man was tending his goats near the rugged shores of the Dead Sea. He noticed one goat was missing. As he searched the rocky terrain, he entered a cave. There he found clay jars with ancient scrolls inside. The scrolls were copies of many old books. Some of them were old copies of parts of the Hebrew Bible. Scholars believe these long-lost scrolls were hidden about 1900 years before they were found.

SPOTLIGHT

The words *terrain, terrace,* and *territory* all have a Latin root meaning *earth* or *land.* Egypt, Greece, Rome, and the area where the Dead Sea Scrolls were found are all located near the Mediterranean Sea. If *medi* comes from a word meaning *middle,* what do you think the name of the Mediterranean Sea means?

Copy and chunk the passage. Look at the opposite page if you need help.

Some of the world's treasures have been

Some

found by accident. One example is the

Dead Sea Scrolls. A young man was

tending his goats near the rugged shores

of the Dead Sea. He noticed one goat

was missing. As he searched the rocky

terrain, he entered a cave. There he

found clay jars with ancient scrolls

inside.

1. Read the passage aloud to your instructor.

2. Mark all six letter patterns that you have learned. They are **vowel chunks** (yellow), **consonant chunks** (blue), **Bossy _r_ chunks** (purple), **Tricky _y_ Guy** (green), **endings** (pink or red), and **silent letters** (orange).

Vowel Chunks	Consonant Chunks	Bossy _r_	Endings
aa ae ai ao au aw ay	ch gh sh ph th wh	ar	-ed
ea ee ei eo eu ew ey eau	wr gn kn dg qu ck	er	-es
ia ie ii io iu	tch bb cc dd ff gg	ir	-ful
oa oe oi oo ou ow oy	hh kk ll mm nn pp	or	-ing
ua ue ui uo uu uy	rr ss tt ww vv zz	ur	-ly

Some of the world's treasures have been found by accident. One example is the Dead Sea Scrolls. A young man was tending his goats near the rugged shores of the Dead Sea. He noticed one goat was missing. As he searched the rocky terrain, he entered a cave. There he found clay jars with ancient scrolls inside. The scrolls were copies of many old books. Some of them were old copies of parts of the Hebrew Bible. Scholars believe these long-lost scrolls were hidden about 1900 years before they were found.

Section 2: First Dictation

Write this week's passage from dictation. Ask for help if you need it.

Some

18E

1. Read the passage aloud to your instructor.

2. Mark all six letter patterns that you have learned. They are **vowel chunks** (yellow), **consonant chunks** (blue), **Bossy *r* chunks** (purple), **Tricky *y* Guy** (green), **endings** (pink or red), and **silent letters** (orange).

Vowel Chunks	Consonant Chunks	Bossy *r*	Endings
aa ae ai ao au aw ay	ch gh sh ph th wh	ar	-ed
ea ee ei eo eu ew ey eau	wr gn kn dg qu ck	er	-es
ia ie ii io iu	tch bb cc dd ff gg	ir	-ful
oa oe oi oo ou ow oy	hh kk ll mm nn pp	or	-ing
ua ue ui uo uu uy	rr ss tt ww vv zz	ur	-ly

Some of the world's treasures have been found by accident. One example is the Dead Sea Scrolls. A young man was tending his goats near the rugged shores of the Dead Sea. He noticed one goat was missing. As he searched the rocky terrain, he entered a cave. There he found clay jars with ancient scrolls inside. The scrolls were copies of many old books. Some of them were old copies of parts of the Hebrew Bible. Scholars believe these long-lost scrolls were hidden about 1900 years before they were found.

Section 2: Second Dictation

See if you can write this week's passage from dictation without asking for help.